With Rifle and Plow

"Coo-wigh! Coo-wigh!" he had called, remembering how the Indians gave their alarm halloo.

With Rifle & Plow

STORIES OF THE
WESTERN PENNSYLVANIA FRONTIER

By

J. E. WRIGHT

ELISABETH M. SELLERS

JEANETTE C. SHIRK

———

ILLUSTRATED BY

ALEXANDER ROSS

PITTSBURGH, PA.

UNIVERSITY OF PITTSBURGH PRESS

1938

6

DEC 21 1939

J g. The Buhl Foundation - Pittsburgh

THESE STORIES of frontier Pennsylvania beyond the mountains, while they have the form of fiction, are based upon fact. The selection of subjects was made from the wealth of historical lore gathered by the staff of the Western Pennsylvania Historical Survey, which was sponsored jointly by The Buhl Foundation, the Historical Society of Western Pennsylvania, and the University of Pittsburgh. The stories are here presented in the hope that young readers will be afforded a glimpse into the past of a region that since the beginning has occupied a strategic place in the councils of empire and industry.

Contents

With Rifle and Plow

· [I] ·

King of the Traders

I N THE deepest part of the woods the traveler stopped his horse
and listened. Dusk settled early over the forest floor: there
was a whir of wings, the soft scuttling of a rabbit into its
hole, the snapping of a dried twig near at hand. The timid forest
creatures hunted cover. Soon wolves would prowl. Owls would
mourn. There might be hunters in the woods. Or Indians.

The traveler had stopped under an oak tree. A few steps away
there was a little spring welling up from the rocks. There was a
small glade where he could build a fire and sleep.

"Steady, boy, steady," he said, as he put leather hobbles on his
horse and loosened the load.

At once he turned his attention to making a fire. After the
flame caught he took from the overlapping folds of his yellow
hunting jacket a piece of dried venison, a chunk of bread, and a
screwed-up paper of salt. With his hunting knife he cut the bread
and venison into small portions, squeezed them together, and
thrust them hungrily into his mouth. After the first bite he
settled himself on a log and leaned against the trunk of the oak
tree, spread his legs in front of him, and studied his moccasins.

"Worn through, just as I thought. Lucky I'm near to Logstown.
They won't stand much more of stones and rough going."

Although he had ridden most of the way from the fort, he had had to walk many miles during the past few weeks, while he inspected his trading posts and talked privately with individual Indians and trusted white helpers. His leggings were cracked and split and generously caked with river clay. His leather shirt was jagged with briars. He pulled off his cap, an ordinary coonskin, and from the inside of it took a mat of tobacco. He stuffed his pipe and set it to smoking with a smoldering brand from the fire. There was nothing so comfortable as a good fire and a pipe of fragrant tobacco.

By this time the evening light had faded completely in the shadow of the forest. Using his log for a back rest, the trader stretched himself on the ground in the glow of the fire. He threw a handful of dried twigs on the dwindling flame and puffed at his pipe. His thoughts turned to the post at Logstown.

"Croghan's" was written over that place. And "Croghan's" was over a dozen other trading posts scattered about the wilderness—Piqua, Pine Creek, Oswegle Bottom, Beaver Creek, Sandusky.

Trader Croghan liked to reflect on his success, to run through the names of his storehouses, and to picture their supplies stacked high—bales, boxes, barrels, bags, every sort of merchandise imaginable. He liked to think of the kegs of rum in the dark corners, and the stacks of arms beside them, the barrels of gunpowder, the pigs of lead that would be melted down for bullets, the boxes of flints, the tomahawks tied in half dozens and hung from the rafters, the packages of vermilion war paint that his Indian customers bartered for so eagerly. George Croghan felt proud and important. He was a trader king. The piles of folded strouds, or blankets, of deep blue and bright red, the matchcloth in rolls and bundles tied together with deerskin thongs, the rolls of linen and calico of the brightest and most flashing colors— these were possessions a wilderness king dreamed of. The furs they would buy would make him a man of consequence, even by standards that existed across the water in the mother country.

"Traps, axes, files, and awls," thought Croghan, "knives of every size and kind, brass wire, rings, and silver jewelry, looking glasses and combs, needles and thread, and buttons of metal and bone. Jew's-harps, whistles and bells!" He gave up counting. These things were only a small part of his wealth—freight that he sent up and down the trails by his pack trains, ten, twenty horses or more, each tied securely to the one in front by a line of rope, and each bearing a bale of merchandise on either side of its packsaddle. Through woods and over streams, winter or summer, into every corner of the wilderness they traveled. From the frontier came great bales of skins, deer, elk, buffalo, and bear, sorted and bound together. Furs of beaver, wolf, raccoon, fox, mountain cat, muskrat, mink, fisher—he let his mind run over all his great stores. There was wealth—yet here he sat in the rough clothes of a hunter, one of his moccasins worn through.

He laughed at this. His eyes twinkled. At the end of a year he could write at the bottom of a great column of figures, running down page after page in his ledger, ten thousand pounds—a fabulous sum in 1749.

Trader Croghan. Rather, King Croghan!

This wealth of his, of what use was it to him? What better thing could a trader do with his money than build warehouses for the storage of his skins and furs? To enhance the value of the skins, what better thing could he do than build a tanyard to cure them himself? And even a traveler needed a house sometimes. Where should a trader build his home, if not at the place where all the traffic from the East and the West must pass near his door? Croghan's was a landmark. It was on all the maps, equally important with Carlisle and Shippensburg.

Trader Croghan had built his fine home on a tract of a thousand acres near Harris' Ferry, which is now Harrisburg. There he could keep his eye on the wilderness caravans. There he provided a stopping point for the emissaries of trade and politics on their way to and from the West, a place where Indians and white traders made a practice of meeting. There, too, he reckoned up his accounts. To that place went his agents from the log storehouses at Sandusky, Piqua, Pine Creek, at Oswegle Bottom on the Youghiogheny, at Logstown eighteen miles below the forks of the Ohio, and from the post at the mouth of Beaver Creek.

The storehouses built for Croghan's convenience along the water routes to the West attracted settlers to those regions. At Pine Creek a number of log houses had sprung up near that convenient post. There Trader Croghan kept some bateaux and canoes. There, too, he had cultivated ten acres of Indian corn, and broad fields had been cleared and fenced as pasture for his horses and cattle.

At Venango John Fraser was trying to start a trading house and gunsmith shop, cutting in on Croghan's fur trade. Fraser was a good man and a canny Scot, but Croghan did not fear his competition.

"From the paved streets of Philadelphia to the last Indian hut beyond Sandusky, there's not a place I haven't been," thought Croghan. "There's not a spot I don't know. To the very palisades of Detroit!"

But here his face clouded. Two of his men who had been trad-

With a quick lunge Trader Croghan split the
barrel, and the rum flowed over the ground.

ing near Detroit had been carried off to Quebec by the French
and then shipped to France.

"That was bad business," thought Croghan. "God knows
where they are now or what has happened to them! Everything
depends on the British ambassador at Paris. If he can't have them
released . . . "

That was out of his hands now. But whatever happened, he
was determined to have the Indian trade around Detroit despite
the hostility of the French. He loved a good contest, and he was
usually successful in dealing with the Indians.

"I'll win them over!" he thought, his eyes glowing. "Those
Frenchmen disgrace the very name of trader. For an Indian's
beaver skin they offer a charge of powder and a single bullet. An
outrage! No wonder the Indian killed that trader with his
hatchet on the spot. He was justified. They can't trade that way."

Trader Croghan dealt fairly with his customers, whether they
were Indian or white. He took a pardonable pride in his diplomacy. He loved to bargain and persuade. He would see the
Indians and talk to them in all fairness, and the French would
find out a thing or two about trading.

"Those French frogs will croak on a different note," thought
Trader Croghan. "Yes," and his head began to nod, "I've not
done too badly for myself. Fifty men. Two hundred pack horses.
And a fair profit in the eight years since I left Ireland!"

He unrolled his blanket, gave a last look around him, listened
for strange sounds and then, hearing nothing, dropped his thick
body down on the ground by the fire. Soon he was fast asleep.

At dawn Croghan was wakened by a crackling of brush. He
leaped up, his hand on his gun. A startled doe bounded away.

"Time to be on my way," thought Croghan, stirring up the

fire, and while he grilled his bacon and ate his johnnycake his thoughts again turned to his empire of trade. "I built up my own trade," he reasoned, "but maybe I'd do well to concern myself with Mr. Trent. He's a right seeming sort of man. Mr. Robert Callender and Mr. Michael Teaffe, too. Three men should be able to do three times what one man alone does. And there's profit and plenty to be had if they work straight with me."

Trader Croghan knew other men who worked in partnership. There were the five Lowrey brothers. They had managed to make themselves fairly rich with their own pack-horse commerce. And the two Jews, Joseph Simon and Levi Andrew Levy, had lately been active at the forks of the Ohio, with a fair success. James Young and John Fraser were another combination. And the three Mitchells, too. And then there were rumors of the foundation of a company of speculators in Virginia—the Ohio Company, it was called. That sounded like formidable competition.

"I'll come to some sort of an understanding with them," Croghan assured himself. "There're plenty of acres open for working between the mountains and Fort Miami. And plenty of beavers along the streams."

He prepared to resume his journey. Then he remembered that he wanted to send a letter to his eastern agent, Mr. Lawrence. Any hour now he might meet some trader or traveler who could deliver it to the Philadelphia office.

With difficulty he scratched out his message on a piece of paper spread on his knee.

"I will Send you down the thousand weight of Sumer Skins Directly, by first waggon I Send Down, I have Gott two hundred pisterns and som beeswax To Send down to you, as you and I was talking of, To Send To Madera."

Trader Croghan had never found that poor spelling and misplaced capitals injured his business! He put the letter in his shirt, unhobbled his horse, and scattered the ashes of his fire. He was on the last lap of his journey.

Some hours later the guns at Logstown fired a salute. Only important persons were welcomed with a salute from the town, and Trader Croghan wondered if this mark of respect was being shown to him. But as he rode toward the Indian village of scattered log houses he felt excitement in the air. Was that singing he heard? It sounded like the choir on a Sunday in the Irish cathedral that he had used to attend years ago. He quickened his pace. He was sure that he heard chanting. But the Indians at Logstown knew no chants!

Nearer the town there was no mistaking the sound. Men's voices they were—and there must be a hundred of them—chanting the *Te Deum*. When Croghan reached the first house he saw that the whole population had gathered at the bank of the river. At the edge of the crowd he saw Henry Norland, a trader whom he heartily disliked.

"What's this?" Croghan shouted, and Norland turned at the question.

"Croghan! It's you! And it's a pity you weren't here an hour sooner. The French devils came down two days ago, saying the river and the land were theirs. Planted lead plates everywhere—claiming the country for their king, they say. Praying and singing all the time. Well, we'll see which king has the best say in this matter!"

"That we will," said Trader Croghan.

He pushed his way through the crowd to the shore, his anger rising. Then he stood awestruck at the sight before him.

Drifting out into the current of the river, a flotilla of canoes and other river craft bore the chanting soldiers of France. At the head of the procession was a great canoe, regal in its appearance. Standing erect at its prow were two figures, one in the uniform of a French officer, the other in the robes of a priest. The bright sunlight flickered about the moving canoes and gleamed on the officers' buttons and braid. It caught the blade of an unsheathed sword and blazed radiantly on a tall silver cross. Row after row of canoes filled with men chanting the *Te Deum* swung out into the river. When the chant came to an end every voice was raised in a mighty shout:

"Vive la France! Vive le Roi!"

Trader Croghan stood speechless, consumed with silent wrath. He could do nothing to prevent this procession of blue-uniformed Frenchmen in their painted canoes, with their silver crosses and upraised swords, with their chanting and their planting of lead plates. They drifted triumphantly down the broad river between the green hills he knew so well and looked upon as his own country—the country he was winning for the English by his fair trading with the Indians.

No, he could do nothing. What could a trader do? Governors, ambassadors, kings settled these questions of possession—usually by a war. What could a trader do?

Trader Croghan knew that these Indians were friendly to the English. Well, they must be kept so. Perhaps winning this wilderness for England could be accomplished more easily by good honest trading than by the planting of plates. There was a delicate bit of diplomacy a trader could exercise, and Croghan made up his mind to use every means in his power to conciliate the Indians, to persuade them to look upon the English as brothers. Yes, a trader might do much for his country.

Croghan made his way to his warehouse. Conrad Weiser came and shook hands cordially. This man was a brother to the Indians, trying to understand them and giving up his life to the arduous task of promoting good relations between them and the whites.

"One of the local traders leaves in an hour," said Conrad Weiser. "Do you have letters to send East?"

"Yes, I have one written, but perhaps I should write a report for Governor Hamilton and send it in as great haste as possible," answered Croghan.

"We'll talk later, then," said Weiser.

Croghan stopped to speak to the Indians who had gathered to stare at the huge packs strapped to his saddle. A word or two was enough. Soft words were never lost on these people. They understood that the white trader had letters to write now, but that the packs would be opened before evening.

Croghan went into his log house, pushed aside the few skins spread on the rough table, took down the inkhorn from the mantelpiece, and composed a letter to Richard Peters, secretary of the provincial council:

"I am Just return^d from the woods and has brought a Letter a French Scalp and some Wompom for ye Governor from a part of ye Six Nations Ingans That has thire Dweling on ye borders of Lake Arey [*Erie*] and not being able To go Down My Self So Soon after Such a Long Journey I have fourthwith Sent itt by the Bearer . . . Those Ingans were always in the French Interest Till Now Butt This Spring allmost all the Ingans in the Woods have Declared against ye french & I Think this will be a fair Opertunity if purshued by some Small Presents, to have all ye french Cutt off in them parts for the Ingans are very Much Led by Any

Thing that will Tend to their own Self Interest and will think a
Great Tail [*deal*] of a Little powder and Lead att This Time . . .
I remain with respect y^r humble Servant to Comm^d."

Croghan enclosed two letters written to Governor Hamilton
by his own hand at the dictation of two of the Indian chiefs.
Croghan had previously told the governor he had complained
to the Indians that their young men were too often seen visiting
the French at the trading posts. He smiled now as he read again
the last sentences of one of the letters:

"It is true some of our Young Men go to pay the French a visit
now and then, and Brothers we assure You that we resent the
abuses done to You & us by the French. We send you this French
Sculp as a token that we don't go to visit them for nothing."

Trader Croghan was sending on to the governor the French
scalp the young Indians had taken.

The letters safely on their way East, the trader ordered his
packs brought into the storehouse. Every inhabitant of the
village was curious about the contents of the trader's packs. They
knew, too, that a pack train had come for him the day before,
and that it probably brought presents as well as the usual articles
for barter.

That evening a great fire was built in the village. A council
was called. The Indians came in their blankets and feathers to
hear what Trader Croghan had to say to them and to see what
gifts he had brought.

The diplomatic trader knew how to create a dramatic effect
with his merchandise. He had blankets spread by the fire, and
on their red and blue backgrounds he scattered the gifts he had
to distribute. The firelight flickered over the seated Indians,
deepening the red-bronze of the intent faces, vivifying the reds

and blues of the blankets, picking out the streaks of white in the black eagle feathers. Quivering shadows danced over the merchandise George Croghan had artfully spread before him. There were kegs of powder hooped with iron bands. There were lead bars for bullets. Long-handled knives glittered and shone, dozens of them laid in rows. There were sheaves and bundles of tobacco. Packages were tied and stacked in half dozen lots. Some of these the trader opened to show their contents: war paints of vermilion, green, blue; tinkling wire bracelets and glass beads; ruffled shirts and petticoats; ribbons of every color and size.

Trader Croghan knew the power of these presents. Their glitter and color he knew to be far more important than their value. Powder and lead and knives were expensive gifts, but tobacco and vermilion were cheaper and easier to transport. They not only made a fine showing, but they brought their value, pressed down and running over, in friendliness, in trade protection, and in lands for settlement.

At such councils Croghan felt like a king indeed. Here at this council fire he held threads of destiny in his hands—a thread to each of three empires, the French, the English, and the Indian. It gave him a thrill of power to guide these Indians the way he thought they should go. He felt he was responsible not only for the present, but for the future as well. At this wilderness outpost of civilization cabins would be built, land plowed, forests cleared. He felt that he was the vanguard of that future.

Gathered about the council fire were fifteen hundred Indians. Scarouady and Tanacharison the Half King, were there. Grave and inscrutable, they waited to hear Croghan's words and to receive the gifts from the White Brother in Philadelphia. The trader sorted the merchandise into piles—powder casks, bars of lead, knives, and boxes of vermilion. The chiefs came forward to receive their share. They handed the white man strings of wampum in token of their good will.

There was talk of the French visit. No gifts had been left by the singing Frenchmen. Not so much as a blanket had been given to the Indians in the name of the French king. There was a sullen resentment among the red men. The allegiance of these tribes was safe.

Then the Indians guilelessly asked for English rum. Not for themselves. Oh, no, they knew the evil of this rum! But another nation of Indians was deserting the French and pledging allegiance to the British. Trader Croghan smiled to himself as he listened to this speech:

"We have heard you have forbid the sale among our tribes of strong liquors, which we approve very well, for we have suffered considerably by such abuses—for there are many people who bring nothing else but liquor and so cheat us of our skins. And many of our people have lost their lives. But, Brother, we have one thing to acquaint you with, that is that there is a great nation of Indians come from the French to be your brothers as well as ours, who say they never tasted English rum yet, but would be very glad to taste it now as they are come to live with the English. So we hope you will order some of your traders to bring them some, for which request we give you this string of wampum."

Trader Croghan had not been in the village an hour before he knew that one of the traders had been selling rum in his absence. He had asked no questions and had made no comments. He had his suspicions, but he could wait.

Now at the mention of rum, Trader Norland could not resist the opportunity to make a sale.

"I've an eight gallon cask," said he. "I'll be glad to put it at Mr. Croghan's service for a certain sum, if he wishes to send it north to that new nation of Indians."

Yes, Croghan's suspicions were confirmed. Norland was the guilty one.

"You can bring me the barrel, Mr. Norland," he said, appearing to agree. "And Mr. Weiser, may I ask you to do me a favor?"

It took some minutes to roll the barrel into the council ring before Trader Croghan. Mr. Weiser returned from his errand at the same time.

"The ax, Mr. Croghan," he said, handing him the implement.

With a quick lunge Trader Croghan split the barrel, and the rum flowed over the ground.

Norland gasped. His face turned red with shame and anger.

The Indians stared, expressionless, stoical.

"There, Mr. Norland," said Trader Croghan quietly, "that is the way we serve your illegal liquor!"

Scarouady and Tanacharison grunted approval. Trader Croghan was there to protect them. They understood what he had done. They respected him. They knew that Indians who dealt with Trader Croghan would never be cheated. Rum was bad for Indians. It dulled their senses. It made them do foolish things. Trader Croghan treated them wisely and fairly. He was a good man. He was English. Well, they would stand by the English. The Indians and the English would be brothers.

Next morning Trader Croghan talked with the chiefs and the friendly Indians.

"We have something to do, Mr. Weiser and I," he said. "Let us go to Mr. Weiser's house."

Before the door of Weiser's log house there grew a tall, slender sapling. One of Croghan's men had cut away the branches.

"The French may plant their lead plates where they will," said Trader Croghan, "but here on this staff we will raise our flag!"

Up rode the flag of Britain. It fluttered and unfurled in the breeze from the river. It flew free and brave, over the heads of the Indians.

Trader Croghan felt his heart swell with pride.

"Even a trader may do his bit for king and country," he thought to himself.

The Indians grunted with approval.

·[2]·

Ensign Ward Surrenders

I<small>N HIS</small> log house at Pine Creek, on an afternoon at the end of
May, 1753, sat George Croghan with his two partners, Mr.
Callender and Mr. Teaffe, and two friendly Indian chiefs.
Tanacharison, the Iroquois chief who as Half King ruled over
the Delawares and the Mohican of the Ohio Valley. His residence
was at Logstown, where also lived Scarouady, the Iroquois chief
who governed the Shawnee. From that village on the north bank
of the Ohio, near where the town of Ambridge now stands, these
two sachems, feathered and robed, had gone to Croghan's house
at Pine Creek to discuss the French claims to the region.

The French! Even then they were marching from Niagara
towards the Ohio, hoping to drive out the English traders and
to build French forts—hoping, in fact, to take over the whole
valley for France and the French king.

Trader Croghan smoothed out a sheet of paper on the table
and dipped his quill in the inkpot.

Sunlight came through the open doorway of the log warehouse. It picked out piles of skins in the corner, the huge iron
pot in the cave-like hearth, the musket and powder horn hanging
over the chimney on elk horns. It fell on the blanketed shoulders
and feathered heads of the Half King and Scarouady, and on the

rough features of Trader Croghan, weathered almost as red brown as the faces of the chiefs. This matter of the French invasion was of serious concern to these men. Their faces were grim.

"Say to the Great White Brother that the English will be safe as long as the Indian will be safe; Tanacharison and Scarouady have said it."

This message was to Governor Hamilton in Philadelphia. George Croghan wrote that the two sachems had declared their reception of the French would depend on the attitude of the French themselves. It would be prudent to prepare the Indians for violence, however, and guns and ammunition were needed.

Trader Croghan folded the paper, sealed it with wax, and handed it to Mr. Callender to be carried at once to the governor. Callender and Teaffe crossed the river and took the trail through the wilderness to the East.

The message they carried from the sachems brought an immediate result. The Pennsylvania Assembly voted eight hundred pounds for guns and ammunition for the friendly Indians on the Ohio. But for three months Governor Hamilton withheld the money.

Tanacharison and Scarouady asked each other, "What shall we do?"

"Maybe our Pennsylvania brothers are too weak for the French," they said, tired of waiting. "It may be good to write to the Great White Brother in Virginia."

So they wrote to Governor Dinwiddie in Virginia for the needed help against the French. But the Virginia governor also delayed. In September a delegation of one hundred Indians journeyed to Winchester, Virginia, to request aid, but to no avail.

From Logstown the Indians sent a message to the French:

"Your children on the Ohio are alarmed to hear of your coming so far this way. We at first heard that you came to destroy us. Our women left off planting and our warriors prepared for war. We have since heard that you came to visit us without design to hurt us, but then we wondered you came with so strong a body. If you have any cause of complaint you might have spoken with the governors of New York and Pennsylvania, and not come here to disturb us. We have a council fire at Logstown, where are the Delawares and Shawnee, and Brother Onas, governor of Pennsylvania. You might have sent deputies there and said openly what you came about, if you thought amiss of the English being there, and we invite you to do it now before you proceed any farther."

"We send no deputies to you," answered the French. "Under order of our king we come to build forts, one at Venango, one at the forks of the Ohio, one at Logstown, and one at Beaver Creek."

Tanacharison, desperate, answered this message in person.

"We forbid you to come any farther. Turn back, to the place you came from," he commanded boldly.

But he was disdainfully received. The French went on with their plans.

The brave Indian chief did not know what to do then. No help from Pennsylvania. None from Virginia. And the French were openly hostile. The Half King returned to Logstown in sorrow. All he could do for his English allies was to warn their traders not to come into the region. It was no longer safe.

In January Trader Croghan made his way to Logstown over snow-covered hills and a frozen river. Andrew Montour and John Patten went with him to learn from their Indian friends the activities of the French in the Ohio Valley.

"You see everything," said Tanacharison. "The French soldiers are here. The Indians drink French brandy. It is bad."

The Frenchmen eyed Trader Croghan with hostility, and he was not allowed to confer with his Indian friends. Croghan was hot tempered. He disliked this treatment. When he protested, the French took John Patten prisoner.

Perhaps this was a warning, a display of authority. Tanacharison effected Patten's release, but the incident increased the bad feeling between French and Indians.

Even with the French soldiers in their town, Tanacharison and Scarouady were determined to resist.

They sent another message to Governor Dinwiddie.

"We ask our brother the governor to build a strong house at the forks of Mohongialo, and send some of his young warriors to live in it. And we expect our brother of Pennsylvania will build another strong house somewhere on the river, where he shall think proper, where whatever help he may think proper to send us will be kept for us, as our enemies are close at hand, and we do not know what day they may come upon us."

"Our brother of Pennsylvania" seemed very remote, very indifferent. Andrew Montour in Philadelphia tried to impress upon the governor the fact that the Indian towns were under his jurisdiction and within the limits of his province, but the Assembly was slow to take up the frontier problems. The frontier was too far removed. Its affairs could not be urgent. The trespassing of the French was as much the concern of Virginia as of Pennsylvania. The matter rested.

But the brother in Virginia?

Yes, at last he set his forces working.

The Ohio Company had been organized by the Virginians

to buy and sell the land in the Ohio Valley and to encourage settlement there. The key to possession of the country was the point where the Allegheny and Monongahela rivers joined to form the Ohio River. The French were already on their way to that point.

Governor Dinwiddie was a stockholder in the Ohio Company. He was actively interested in establishing a definite English claim to the district.

"Proceed to the forks of the Ohio," he commanded Captain William Trent by letter, "there to raise a fort."

Captain Trent was at Redstone (later Brownsville). At the end of January he had started to erect a log storehouse for the Ohio Company. He had seventy men with him, and, although the storehouse was not completed, he and his men moved on to the point of land at the forks of the Ohio. Forty miles of wet tramping through ice and snow and deep wilderness. Up the two rivers and down the third, not a sign of habitation could be seen. High wooded hills rose on every side.

On the high bank above the meeting place of the rivers a great fire was built. Tanacharison and Scarouady gathered with the Englishmen.

Help at last!

Gifts of lead, powder, hatchets, and the cherished vermilion with which the Indians loved to smear themselves were spread out on blankets. The white brothers from Virginia would build a strong house here, if Tanacharison and Scarouady would help them to keep out the Frenchmen who were threatening to take possession of the land.

Tanacharison and Scarouady pledged themselves. They offered to help build the strong house.

Captain Trent at once gave orders to begin cutting down trees. Seating himself on a log by the fire, he laid a board over his knees and set to work drawing a rough plan of the fort. Before the short February day had drawn to a close and the hills and rivers began to merge into shadows, a fair-sized clearing had been made on the plain in the fork of the rivers. Felled trees lay everywhere, waiting to be squared or dragged away for firewood, or to have their branches lopped off for palisades. The blunt nose of land looked strangely bare, jutting into the water against a landscape of trees.

The next day Captain Trent directed the laying out of the fort. The Indians helped by sorting and carrying the logs as they were squared, by making convenient piles on the four sides where the walls were to be. The winter sunlight warmed the men as they worked. As the ground was cleared squirrels scampered into the woods, and once a bear lumbered out from the edge of the clearing.

Tanacharison and Scarouady laid the first log of the fort.

"This fort belongs to the English and to us," they said. "Whoever offers to prevent its building, we will make war against him."

Thus began the erection of Fort Prince George, the first fort in the wilderness around the forks of the Ohio. Captain Trent's men set about placing the logs according to his plan.

In Virginia, Governor Dinwiddie could now feel that his interests in the land of the Ohio Company were being protected.

But Captain Trent had brought few supplies from Redstone. The Indians who had promised to supply the Virginians with meat and game failed to do so. Rather, they complained constantly of the small number of men who had come to help protect the Ohio Valley.

"Too few men," they said. "Indians not very many, but English no help at all when French come."

Captain Trent grew impatient. The Indians were not helping as they had promised, and they used up the supply of flour and meal and constantly demanded more. They asked for powder and lead as well. And their interest in the erection of the log walls of the fort gradually dwindled. Captain Trent was very anxious to get the work finished. Conditions were deplorable. His men were weak from lack of food, the weather was unpleasant, the work was heavy, and the men were not pleased with the pay they were receiving from the Ohio Company. Trent tried to pacify his group in every way. He felt he did not care how little money he himself received if only he could finish the fort.

Good news heartened the captain. Christopher Gist sent word from his plantation at Redstone that Major Washington was on his way to join Captain Trent.

One day Tanacharison came to the fort.

"The English are too few," he said bluntly. "You cannot hold this fort or help the Half King and Scarouady with so few warriors. If the Virginia warriors come, good. Go quickly to the settlement for soldiers."

Captain Trent knew the Half King spoke wisely. He would go back to Wills Creek for aid. He looked about for someone to leave in command of the unfinished fort.

He chose Ensign Edward Ward, George Croghan's half brother. If necessary, Ensign Ward could enlist help from the Delaware Indians through an appeal to the trader.

Captain Trent left, taking half the men with him to bring back supplies. Work at the fort went very slowly.

One day Christopher Gist arrived. He saw at once the poor

conditions and knew that unless the men were properly fed the work on the fort could not go on.

"Give me some of your men," he said to Ensign Ward. "They can go back with me for supplies. Word comes every now and then that the French are coming down the Allegheny. The fort must be hurried to completion, but your men need food. I will send you supplies."

This seemed wise to do. Ensign Ward sent a number of men with Christopher Gist.

They had hardly left before a runner came with fateful news.

"The French are coming! Three hundred canoes! A thousand men! Fifty bateaux! Brass cannon!"

"Where are they now?" demanded Ensign Ward. He thought, sickly, of his handful of men.

"At Venango and Le Bœuf. They were preparing to embark. They will be here in a few days."

The work at the fort went desperately on. Days of work, when weeks were needed. Would any help come from Trent? From Gist? From anywhere? Major Washington, where was he? Trader Croghan! How to get word to him?

From Shannopin's Town two miles up the Allegheny came word of the arrival of the French fleet. Two miles away.

Two miles away!

Ensign Ward placed his men in readiness. Less than forty men. To hold an unfinished fort!

He looked at the point of land that meant so much. It was the key to the vast stretch of country between Wills Creek on the south and Fort Le Bœuf on the north, between the mountains and the three rivers. The fort's importance was out of all proportion to its size. To hold it meant to hold the whole country for his king. To lose it meant to lose the whole vast region.

Two of his men came running from the woods.

"They are landing!" they shouted, breathlessly. "A hundred canoes at least! They have struck the banks and are forming ranks to march on us!"

Even as the men spoke the fleet of bateaux swept around the bend in the river.

"La France! Pour la France!" shouted the boatmen.

Almost at once, through the trees beyond the uncompleted palisades of logs, came the French soldiers. They halted at a distance, and from the ranks an officer accompanied by an Indian interpreter came forward.

Ensign Ward stood waiting.

The white flag of truce fluttered before the French officers. There was a sound of beating drums. There were shouts from the bateaux on the river as the fleet steered in toward the bank. Mechanically Ensign Ward returned the salute of the young French officer. The Frenchman spoke, and his words rattled from his lips like shot. Ensign Ward knew the import of the message before the impassive Indian had translated it:

"Lieutenant le Mercier has the honor to demand for his commander in chief, Captain Contrecœur, the immediate surrender of the fort."

Le Mercier looked at his watch.

"The hands stand at two. In one hour you will have made your decision. Do us the honor of waiting upon Captain Contrecœur in the French camp with the decision in writing."

Ensign Ward knew that his position was hopeless. He conferred with Tanacharison, and after some discussion the Half King made a suggestion.

"Request the French captain to await the arrival of the commander of the fort. Tell the French captain that you are not of sufficient rank as an officer to answer the demands."

That would do little good, thought Ensign Ward. But it was something to say. Something to delay the fatal words he knew he must say in the end.

They made their way to the French camp.

Captain Contrecœur received them with professional military courtesy. Inwardly he must have been amused at Ward's reply, but his look and his voice were steel.

Wait for a commandant? That was out of the question. He would seize the fort and everything in it, unless the ensign surrendered voluntarily and immediately.

Ensign Ward was aware of the forces against him. From where he stood he could see scores of canoes moored to the banks below. He saw rank upon rank of French uniforms. And through the trees by the river the sun blazed on brass cannon. There was no sign of help from any quarter. His heart was lead. He hardly heard his own voice.

"I surrender," said Ensign Ward.

He went back to the fort, the unfinished fort that was no longer his, nor his king's, but that now belonged to the King of France. Everything that belonged to his garrison he was allowed to take with him, but he and his men must leave the country in the morning. That night Ensign Ward and his men had to camp three hundred yards outside the fort they had been forced to surrender. The ensign was invited to have dinner with the French captain, a dinner of meat and wines, after days of hunger and aching fatigue. How could he eat this meat and drink these wines? His throat contracted. The French captain hoped to get from him information about the English government's plans.

"With such affairs, sir, believe me, I am totally unacquainted," said Ensign Ward.

Captain Contrecœur offered to buy some of the carpenter's tools in the English garrison.

"They are not my own, they are the king's!" replied the ensign. "We have need of them in our retreat."

"I would pay you well for them," said the captain.

"Sir, my king and my country I love too well to leave one of these tools behind me." And Ensign Ward retired to his camp.

Through the night the French celebrated their victory. *Vive la France!*

Fort Prince George! It had been the outpost of British empire. Now it was just a story to be told—a paragraph in some future history book.

·[3]·

Washington's First Command

"THEY told me," George Washington wrote in his report, "that it was their absolute Design to take Possession of the Ohio—and by G—— they would do it!"

Governor Dinwiddie looked up from his reading, his eyes flashing. He tapped the paper with the back of his hand.

"These words from the French will sting those laggards in New York and Boston," he declared. "And the lords of trade in their fine London houses will not find them over pleasant!"

He read and reread the report from young Washington.

So this was how the French had answered the message Washington had carried to them, the message of the governor under instructions from the king of England, the message insisting that the French leave the Ohio Valley! A thousand miles of unbroken wilderness, two and a half months of cold, wet weather, ice and snow, perilous escapes from death . . . had the trip through the wilderness to the French forts, Venango and LeBœuf, been a fruitless mission?

Washington had found the French extremely courteous, but crafty and determined. There was no doubt about their intentions.

"They exerted every Artifice they could invent to set our own

26

J 917110
W 93 o.2

Washington's First Command

Indians at Variance with us, to prevent their going 'till after our departure. Presents. Rewards . . . "

While the French had been conferring among themselves as to their reply to the message, Washington had carefully studied the fort, jotted down the smallest item of interest, counted the canoes, estimated the strength of the French forces. He had heard complacent conversations about their plans. All the territory as far east as the Susquehanna River was claimed by the French, and a line of French forts was planned to cut off the English settlements. English traders were to be captured or turned out of the country. Four forts were already garrisoned, and as soon as spring came a fort was to be built at the forks of the Ohio. Two hundred and twenty canoes—birch and pine—were ready for the expedition.

Doubt on the part of the English as to the claims and encroachments of the French on the Ohio Valley had vanished. Washington's visit to the forts had cleared the situation of any uncertainty.

"I hope what has been said will be sufficient to make your Honor satisfied with my conduct," wrote Washington, "for that was my aim in undertaking the journey."

Governor Dinwiddie was decidedly satisfied with young Washington and his conduct. In order to arouse the colonies and England he had Washington's journal published far and wide. As the governor apprehended, this led to immediate action. English troops were ordered at once to the forks of the Ohio.

Major Washington had been home from his travels scarcely ten weeks when Governor Dinwiddie ordered him to active duty.

"You will enlist one hundred men, train them, equip them, and with them go out and complete in the best manner and as soon as you possibly can, the fort on the Ohio River already begun by the Ohio Company. You are to act on the defensive, but in case any attempts are made to obstruct the works or interrupt our settlements by any persons whatsoever, you are to make prisoners of, or kill and destroy them."

Active duty would fill his mind, thought the young man in regimental uniform standing before Governor Dinwiddie; drilling and fighting would use his restless energy. He was pleased at the governor's orders, and yet—he was taken by a kind of fright.

He was only twenty-two, this young major, and he had already been on a mission requiring diplomacy and strategy; his report had been published in the colonies and in England; it had reached the ears of the lords of trade in London; his name was spoken there as well as in the colonies; his name was on the lips of His Majesty, the King of England!

He was twenty-two, a commissioned adjutant general of the British colonials with the rank of major, but he had never drilled a soldier nor himself been drilled. He had studied the manual of tactics and warfare with Major Muse, but the mere study of a book on the practice of warfare could not equip a man to stand before troops and command them. Lawrence, his half-brother, had hired a tutor for him and had had him instructed in engineering. Lawrence had also succeeded in getting him a commission with the militia, with the help of their friend Colonel Fairfax. The young major was inexperienced and knew it. He knew also that the French against whom he was being sent belonged to the best-trained armed force of Europe.

Washington began recruiting with misgivings. He found it a difficult task.

"I have increased my number of men to about twenty-five,"

he wrote a month later, "loose, idle persons that are quite desti-
tute of house and home, and I may truly say, many of them of
cloathes . . . There are many of them without shoes, others want
stockings, some are without shirts, and not a few that have scarce
a coat or waistcoat to their backs."

A disheartening sight, these half-clothed, half-starved, discouraged men who were to fight against the French. It was anything but a happy prospect for Washington.

His first command!

Repeated requests for clothing and supplies were waved aside,
but to strengthen the young leader's position with his forces the
governor commissioned Washington a lieutenant colonel. He
wrote:

"Enclos'd You have Commission. Lieut.-Colo. pay, 12s.6d
per day Without any Trouble of Commanding a Comp'y."

The new lieutenant colonel was furious. Instead of an honor,
this was a grievance to him. Why should he receive only half the
salary of a royal commissioned officer? For a while he was tempted
to refuse the commission, even going so far as to consult with
Colonel Fairfax about the matter. Upon the older man's advice,
however, he decided to accept the situation. He rode back to his
command, his half-clothed militia stationed at Alexandria. He
would accept conditions, but he would inform the governor
that he would much rather have had uniforms for his men than
an empty commission that meant nothing more than a name on
a paper. Where were the blue coats to take the place of the piti-
ful outfits his troops were wearing? He appealed to the governor
for clothing and supplies, but all he got from the governor eager
to turn the French away from the Ohio Valley, all that the
governor would give him, were orders and more orders.

"March what soldiers you have enlisted immediately to the Ohio, and escort some Waggons, with the necessary Provisions."

Soldiers! They were self-willed, ungovernable men.

Wagons! Was Washington to beg for them along the way?

Recruits were promised from other provinces, and twenty-four tents were being sent. Picks, cutlasses, and halberds? There were none. The officers were forced to lead companies equipped only with small arms.

"To the Ohio!" It was an immediate command.

"As our cause is just, I hope for the protection of Heaven," said Governor Dinwiddie.

Lieutenant Colonel Washington marched out of Alexandria with his first troops, two companies of foot soldiers commanded by Captain Peter Hogg and Lieutenant Jacob Van Braam. Flags fluttered in the chill April sunlight. With fife and drum playing martial airs, the ragged detachment straggled along the road to Cumberland. They were on their way, on the long march to the forks of the Ohio.

Six miles out of town they halted their two wagons, pitched their tents, and made the first night's camp.

On an evening in mid-April, 1754, Colonel Washington wrote in his journal to record the route and the events of the march. Two weeks on the way, and the detachment was now at Job Pearsal's plantation on the South Branch of the Potomac River. The scantily clad men demanded spirits to quicken their blood and warm them, and Washington spent money from his own purse for them. There was nothing else to do.

As he wrote his accounts, Washington was interrupted. Someone had come from Captain Trent at the forks of the Ohio.

"What news from the fort?" asked Washington eagerly.

"We need men. Send reënforcements with all possible speed. The French are expected any hour!"

"And the fort itself?"

The man shrugged his shoulders.

"Just taking shape," he said. "The stockade is not yet finished. The men are weak and starving. Supplies are exhausted. There is nothing to eat but corn meal and water. Can you send men? Can you send food? With all possible speed!"

The man was haggard looking, tired, and hungry. Washington ordered food for him and a noggin of rum, and at once despatched a messenger to Colonel Fry, his superior, to rush men and arms. Until late that night Colonel Washington sat at his camp table writing in the wavering half-light of his candle to Governor Dinwiddie and noting in his journal the news he had just received.

Early next morning he started on horseback for Colonel Thomas Cresap's plantation on the north side of the Potomac. A new detachment had arrived that morning for his command. As he was on his way a messenger from Ensign Ward caught up with him.

Bad news. The fort had been taken.

"A thousand men they had, those Frenchmen! Hundreds of bateaux and canoes! And only a handful of men at the fort," said the messenger.

Washington was aghast.

The fort taken!

"That may mean an attack upon us also," he thought.

With all his forces he set out for Wills Creek, fifteen miles from Cresap's.

A few days later Ensign Ward appeared, dejected and dismayed. He told all the details of the surrender and how, with Captain Trent absent from the fort, it had been his unhappy lot to yield Fort Prince George to the French.

"The French have the largest force of men and war equipment that the back country has ever seen assembled!" he declared, and his anxiety to excuse his surrender made him exaggerate the strength of the enemy. "A thousand men in the finest uniforms! Hundreds of bateaux and canoes. And cannon. We could not count them! Even with reënforcements we could not have withstood them."

"But the Indians?" asked Washington.

"The Indians want to remain friendly with the English, but unless the English send men and arms in sufficient numbers the French will surely destroy them all."

A council of war was held at Wills Creek. Arguments and discussions lasted all day. By evening it was decided that Colonel Washington should proceed boldly to the place where Redstone Creek empties into the Monongahela River. There the Ohio Company had already erected two storerooms for the furs collected in the Indian trade. Ammunition could be held there in readiness, and artillery could easily be shipped down river when Washington was ready to attack the French at the fort.

Word came through scouts that the French were building a fort, which they had named Fort Duquesne in honor of the governor general of Canada. The construction work would keep them occupied for some time.

Washington at once set his companies to cutting a road for the wagons through the almost impenetrable wilderness that still lay between his encampment and Redstone. There were no more than one hundred and fifty men. A rainy season set in.

Cold days held on. The forest was bare and black, and the undergrowth was scraggy and dense. Chopping, grubbing out stumps, clearing the underbrush, filling hollows, and cutting away banks, the column of men crept forward day by day. The rain fell so heavily that banks washed out as soon as they were cut. Hollows were filled with mud and water. The men sometimes worked in water up to their armpits. Hardly more than a mile a day could be cleared, and by May 9 the troops had reached Little Meadows, only about twenty miles from Wills Creek. The men were hungry. The weather turned cold. Fires were hard to make from the soaked logs and brush. The soldiers grumbled and demanded rum to keep them warm and to stimulate them. The officers who went ahead to lay out the route and to direct the work lost their way in the swamps. They, too, complained to Washington. They, too, demanded better food and more pay. They grew mutinous. They demanded that other officers should be sent to replace them. They had had enough.

Washington heard nothing but grumbling and complaining. There was nothing he could do to help matters. He wrote letter after letter to the governor. Occasionally news reached them. Colonel Fry was at Winchester with one hundred men, and would set out in a few days. Colonel James Innes was coming from Carolina with a force of three hundred and fifty. Pennsylvania could send no recruits but had raised ten thousand pounds to pay soldiers sent by other provinces.

The traders who stopped at the camp brought news.

"The French at the fort have more men than ever. Reënforcements have arrived. And a new force of French soldiers are expected under La Force!"

"The French are near Gist's plantation! We don't know how

many, but scouting parties have been seen there. We just came from that country, and we know it is impossible for you to think of cutting a road through those dense woods and worse than impossible to make a road wide enough to let wagons pass."

In spite of every discouragement, Washington went on with his tremendous task of road building. He reached the Great Crossings of the Youghiogheny River, and there two Indians brought him more news of the French and of Fort Duquesne.

"It is already half-man high," they said. "It is strong and thick. It is filled with earth and stone. The French cut down and burn the trees. They plant corn. They have many men there, and more coming, until they are like the leaves on the trees for number."

The news was disheartening. Always more and more men! Where did they all come from? There seemed to be an inexhaustible supply of Frenchmen. Why was it so difficult to muster Englishmen? Colonel Washington wrote more letters to Governor Dinwiddie. He *must* have more men. He *must* have more food and supplies. He *must* have better food for his officers' tables. He himself was displeased with his pay, which was now two dollars a day.

"I would rather prefer the great toil of a daily laborer and dig for a maintenance . . . than serve upon such ignoble terms," he wrote indignantly.

Why were the lives of His Majesty's subjects in Virginia of less value than the lives of English soldiers in other parts of the American dominions? The Virginians were working under physical hardships; it was hard service and required great personal sacrifice, yet the compensation was but half the amount given soldiers in less dangerous parts of the colonies.

To these complaints Governor Dinwiddie, who had many

troubles of his own, sent a letter of censure. Military hardships were all part of a soldier's lot. He hinted at lack of appreciation of his favors. And to this Washington replied, "Nothing is a greater stranger to my breast, or a sin that my soul more abhors, than that black and detestable one, ingratitude."

There was nothing to be gained, then, by writing to the governor. Colonel Washington shoved his papers aside, screwed the cap on his inkwell, and snapped shut the clasp of his pen case. He threw his cape over his shoulders and went out.

From some distance away came the steady sound of ax blows against tree trunks. It would not be long before the advance cutters caught up with him. His tent was pitched not far from the banks of the Youghiogheny. The river was swollen from the spring rains, and a mountain stream splashing down the slope behind Washington's tent foamed like a waterfall into the churning water of the river below. At least it had stopped raining. Now they could explore the river and determine its feasibility as a route to the Ohio.

With Lieutenant John West, three soldiers, and an Indian, Washington went to the bank where a canoe was turned bottom up. This they righted and lifted into the water, holding it firmly against the low bank until they had taken their places. At once the canoe shot out into the surging river, rising and falling on the rapidly turning current. It shot past an upstanding rock. It scraped a whirling log and tilted dangerously on its side. It shipped a bucket of water. It catapulted into an eddy, where it spun dizzily until violent strokes pushed it into the current again. Vainly the men tried to control the canoe as it leaped through the rough water. They were carried about a mile by the swift current, but no stretch of the wild river offered safe passage. They stopped to construct a strong boat to carry them farther. But at Turkey Foot, now Confluence, the Indian who was with them refused to go on:

"The English do not pay," he said. "The French have Indians to show them the woods, and they pay. I do not go farther."

Washington promised him a ruffled shirt and a matchcoat, and he was instantly appeased.

Thirty miles down the river, however, all hope of a waterway to the forks of the Ohio was abandoned. The falls at Ohiopyle, nearly forty feet high, barred the way. Disappointed, they decided on a convenient ford.

By the afternoon of May 24 the men had reached Great Meadows on the east side of Laurel Hill. There they were met by a trader from Christopher Gist's plantation.

"I saw two Frenchmen last night on my way here," he said, "and I know there is a strong detachment on the march."

Washington hastily ordered two intrenchments constructed, planning to place his troops and his wagons behind them. He sent out scouts, but they returned with no news. How strong was this detachment? And just where were they located? From what direction would they appear?

All night the sentries fired at the cracking of twigs that seemed to indicate prowling figures. But there were no answering shots.

Sunrise revealed that six men had deserted.

Three days passed, three days of uneasiness and watchful apprehension.

Christopher Gist himself brought alarming news.

"Yesterday came some fifty Frenchmen to my house. It was near noon, and they would have killed a cow and broken everything in the house if my two Indians left in charge had not prevented them. Look to them, for they mean no good!"

Seventy-five men were at once sent out in pursuit. Washington enlisted the aid of the Indians by telling them that the French were searching for the Half King, to kill him.

Rain fell steadily. It cast a gloom over everything. The sound of unending drops upon leaves, the puddles between the water-soaked tents, the chilling dampness that gradually crept through the heaviest uniform, and the fog that half hid the hills all around the camp depressed the Virginians. The horses, tethered to the trees, raised their heads and shook their manes as the rain dripped into their eyes and ran down their noses.

Late in the evening came a message from the Half King:

"I have found the place where the whole body of French are hiding!"

At last! Here was something definite. Here was a chance for action.

Forty men were immediately sent out to reconnoiter. A guard was set, lest a surprise attack be made. Ammunition was put in a place of safety behind the crude intrenchments. And Colonel Washington, with the rest of his men, set out for the Half King's camp.

Like Indians, in single file they picked their way over wet ground, the rain beating into their faces, soaking their shoulders and knees, running down their necks. Night came on. Trailing vines caught the men's feet and sent them sprawling, one colliding with another. No one spoke. In the darkness brush crackled, and the moving file stood silent. At times the way was lost. They wandered back and forth aimlessly until they found it again. Over hillocks, into hollows, stumbling and sliding, cautiously stretching their hands to guide them, they felt their way along the worn trail. Their feet were soaked, their faces were scratched by twigs, their coats were torn. Silent, watchful, peering into the rainy darkness, straining their ears to hear any telltale sounds from the unseen enemy, the long line of men made their way through the woods.

At last they could dimly see each other, obscure, bedraggled figures, unfamiliar in the gray of approaching dawn. As the sky whitened they arrived at the Half King's camp. A hasty council was held. Two scouts were sent out and returned very soon. "The French have made a lean-to against a ledge of rock in a ravine," they reported. "It will be easy to surround them!"

Once again the Virginians filed cautiously over the wet hillside, silent and tense. They skirted a deep hollow.

"*Halte!*" The challenge rang sharply from the ravine.

The men stopped. They hardly dared to breathe. They waited silently.

"*Halte! Qui va la?*" A second challenge rang out.

"Fire!" ordered Colonel Washington.

Guns cracked. Twigs snapped. Shouts rang out. White flashes of smoke hung in the air as the bullets whistled by. The men leaped behind trees, pouring their fire down upon the French camp below them.

A quarter of an hour, and the skirmish was over. The circling file of Englishmen closed in. The French surrendered. Their commander, Ensign Coulon de Jumonville, was killed. Lieutenant La Force and twenty-one men gave up their arms. Tomahawks fell, scalping knives flashed—the Indians hastily gathered up the weapons of the dead. With the prisoners under guard, Washington marched back to camp.

The English were elated over their victory. But Washington

felt that the French would lose no time in avenging the death of Jumonville, and he was certain now of a future encounter with a far greater number of soldiers. He lost no time. He dispatched Ensign Towers to the Half King and sent an express to Colonel Fry. Reënforcements!

Under a guard of twenty men he sent the prisoners to Winchester to Colonel Fry. Then he went on with his work. He did not know that Colonel Fry had fallen from his horse near Wills Creek and had died of his injuries. Christopher Gist brought the news when he arrived at camp to report the safe arrival of the French prisoners.

Governor Dinwiddie made Washington a full colonel, but new difficulties instantly arose. Captain Mackay arrived in camp with a company of one hundred Carolina soldiers, better fed and better paid than the troops with Washington. The officers had the advantage of commissions from the king, and they looked with contempt upon the Virginians. The newcomers lolled about camp, joking and drinking, refusing to work on the road except for extra pay, but not averse to watching Colonel Washington's men labor day after day, cutting logs and building. The Virginians resented this heartily. The situation was unbearable. Captain Mackay would not even receive the parole and countersign from Colonel Washington. Colonel Washington's men would not accept commands from Captain Mackay. Finally the two forces separated.

Washington and his men went on with the work of constructing a fort and of cutting a road through the forest, a slow and laborious task. But at the end of June news about the oncoming French troops brought the two English forces together again at Great Meadows. All hands were turned to strengthening the intrenchments and completing the stockade. Washington called their fort, appropriately, Fort Necessity. It was on low ground surrounded by three forested hills where the enemy could easily be concealed and could fire down upon the encampment. The position was unfortunate, unless the French were to march boldly against the fort, across the open meadows. The number of English soldiers was pitifully small, and relations between the two companies were not cordial. Washington, recognizing all this, nevertheless knew that he must make his stand there or retreat.

Early on the morning of the third of July the blue uniforms of the French were sighted behind the trees, and the sentry gave the alarm by firing his gun. Colonel Washington drew up his men in good order before the intrenchments. He ordered them to reserve fire until the attacking French and their Indian allies drew closer. There was no powder to be wasted.

With their Indian allies, the French forces numbered fifteen hundred. The English were about three hundred, and their Indian allies strongly advised a retreat. Many of them acted upon their own suggestion.

With dismal shouts and yells the French advanced towards the camp. A first volley and then a second volley brought no response from the English. The French were within sixty yards of the lines and the shallow valley quivered with their shots. The horses, grazing in the open space back of the intrenchments, stampeded under the fire. The cattle charged wildly over the wet grass. Washington ordered the lines to retire within the trenches, and then he gave the order to fire.

All day the firing continued. In the afternoon a heavy downpour filled the trenches with water. The men slipped and slid in the fresh dug earth. The rain beat down on the two armies.

The swivel guns were dragged to the muddy earthworks, but their wheels sank so deep in the soft clay that the guns were unmanageable. Their shots went wild. The French fire held steady and Washington's gunners could not stand against it. Two Virginians fell. They dragged themselves down the embankment into the water-filled trench, and a dozen Frenchmen ran forward to seize the gun, but at the same time a dozen English soldiers leaped to the top of the bank. Shots cut down men on each side. But the French fire was too sharp, and the guns on the earthworks were abandoned. The wounded Virginians wallowed in the water and mud. From one crude bastion to the other men lay dead in the heavy rain, their arms crumpled under them, their faces buried in the mud.

Mackay's men in the outworks demanded relief.

They swore volubly. "Mud to the knees!"

The ramrods were snapping in two. If they fell they were lost in the mud.

"The powder is wet. It won't pack!"

There was no food. Rum was given out to stimulate the men; their bodies were stiffening with cold.

All afternoon the French refused to come out in the open; they spread out behind their screen of trees, completely surrounding the fort. They drove the cattle and horses to the edge of the forest and slaughtered them. Firing continued unabated.

There was no hope for the English troops, the struggle was too unequal. Though the crude fortification still held, it was only a question of time before the end must come.

When night began to fall the French abated their fire and offered a parley.

"It's a trick," said the English soldiers to one another. "It's one of their French tricks. They just want to get us out in the open!"

They answered with a volley of shots.

Once again the French called out for an officer who could speak French and discuss terms. They shouted their parole for his safe return.

The English were exhausted. They knew they could not hope to hold out much longer. They ceased firing. Who was to go to the French? Peyroney and Van Braam were the only two men acquainted with the French language. Their names were called out in the darkness.

"Chevalier de Peyroney is badly wounded, sir," reported one of the men.

"Then, Lieutenant Van Braam, you will complete the negotiations," directed Washington.

Jacob Van Braam was a fencing teacher and an old soldier from Holland. He did not speak English too well, but he had served as interpreter on Washington's trip to the French forts and had been conscientious and resolute. Washington trusted him implicitly.

Van Braam made his way over the rain-soaked, rain-beaten open space to the French lines and received the proposals for a capitulation. Back at Fort Necessity Colonel Washington lighted his candle time and time again, only to have the wind and rain flick it out and leave the room in darkness. The flint struck with difficulty. It was impossible to write out a translation of the proposal under such conditions. The interpreter read the communication with great difficulty and many interruptions.

The terms of surrender were accepted.

Captain Mackay signed the capitulation first.

Colonel Washington dipped his pen in the inkhorn and with a badly shaking hand added his name on the rain-splashed, blotted paper.

Surrender!

Defeat!

They were bitter words to young Washington.

At sunrise next morning the English troops marched out of Fort Necessity with all the honors of war. The prisoners the English had taken previously were to be delivered up to the French, and Van Braam and another officer were to be kept as hostages until that part of the agreement had been carried out. On the retreat to Wills Creek the enemy Indians annoyed and plundered the English repeatedly, deliberately breaking the terms of the agreement with the French and adding to the misery of the defeated army.

Again the land from the mountains to the Ohio was indisputably in the possession of the French.

Washington went on to Williamsburg. Governor Dinwiddie awaited his report, that fateful report of his first command. . . .

·[4]·

The Three Brothers

WHERE the path turned the brow of a hill a man on horseback stopped under a beech tree to look down into the valley below him. He was a stocky man in black broadcloth coat and leather breeches, hand-knit woolen stockings, and broad beaver hat. He had a long black beard that did not conceal his German features but lent dignity to his appearance.

Israel Eckerlin—or Brother Israel, as he preferred to be known —carried before him on the pommel of his saddle a long rifle. But even in the Monongahela wilderness nearly two hundred years ago this man's trust in God was strong enough to prevent him from using his rifle except to bring down game; he would never defend himself when attacked by hostile Indians or white men, nor would he ever attempt to escape if captured.

A long rope attached to his saddle led a second horse, which bore a large packsaddle.

Daniel the cook and Johann the servant followed. Each wore woolen stockings and leather breeches, black coat, and broad hat, and each carried before him on the saddle a rifle.

Johann, the younger, perhaps nineteen years old, also had a second horse tied to his saddle. On its back were fastened various articles of household furniture—two large stone jugs, some iron kettles, several chairs, and a spinning wheel.

"Daniel," said Brother Israel in German, pointing to a distant place in the valley, "I think we have reached the Turkey Foot Hill. Yonder is the creek Brother Gabriel wrote of and here is his mark blazed on a tree!" He indicated a large cross blazed into the trunk of the beech tree and the initials G. E., for Gabriel Eckerlin, cut below.

"It grieves me that Brother Gabriel uses the initials of his old, worldly name," he continued, more to himself than to his servant. "I had hoped we would hold to the new names we took as brothers in God. Has Gabriel reverted to worldly practices? Has he become estranged from the practices of the Ephrata brotherhood? This shows a resentment against those of the brotherhood who thought fit to cast us out of their community. It shows lack of forgiveness." He shook his head sadly. "We mourn the blindness of man in spiritual matters, but we expose ourselves to the spirit of the world when we harbor resentment against those who have wronged us."

Over the hills in the distance heavy gray clouds were mounting.

"Daniel! Johann! Yonder is Canaan! Brother Gabriel has written me it is a land of milk and honey, for cattle do well and the bees thrive. Sweet red plums are there in abundance. Grapes grow wild and wind around the trees. The pods of the honey locust are sweet when they burst. There are deer aplenty and cock turkeys. The world there is peaceful. Yonder is Canaan. Let us go down."

As the horses picked their way down the stony path into the valley the air grew sultry and still; the clouds rolled heavily, thunderously overhead. The leaves above the heads of the riders were motionless in the breathless pause that comes before a storm. Only the clop of the horses' feet was to be heard in the threatening stillness.

Lightning flashed and thunder rolled. The path became dark and the descent more difficult. By the time the travelers reached the stream, gleaming silver below, heavy drops of rain were rippling its surface.

Suddenly the rain came in a downpour.

"Johann, the capes!" shouted Brother Israel.

The young servant quickly untied the ropes of a leather traveling case and took from it three black rainproof capes. These the riders flung over their shoulders and shook around them hastily. The rain beat against the men and fell in heavy drops from their clothes.

For a while they followed the creek. They came to a place where the bank fell away and the stream, which had gradually broadened, received a smaller stream and spread out suddenly into a shallow bed. After fording the stream and continuing for some distance along the opposite bank, the riders at last reached a stretch of fertile ground, where stood a cabin and several sheds. The heavy rain and the rumble of thunder deadened the sound of their approach, and it was not until Israel knocked at the door that a tall man in buckskin showed himself.

"Brother!" he exclaimed. "You've come!" They kissed each other's cheeks.

"Oh, how long the winter has been," said Gabriel, leading his brother to the fireplace inside the cabin. While Johann hobbled the horses and brought in the boxes and sacks that had been strapped to the saddles, Daniel the cook cut thick steaks of venison and put turnips into the iron pot that swung from the crane over the fire. Israel told of his twelve-day journey from Ephrata through the wilderness west of the Pennsylvania mountains.

"Little did I think the brethren would depose their prior," said Gabriel. "When they ordered me to leave, I forgave them for their blindness to our spiritual teachings. But you, Brother Israel, their prior! To be denounced and dismissed! I confess it angered me."

"It saddened me," said Israel, "and I grieved over the worldliness of the brethren, but everywhere it is the same. Our brother Elimelech was ordered out of Kedar, above Zoar, and he has renounced the world forever."

"A hermit?" asked Gabriel.

"Yes," said Israel. "He is lost to us. We must accept his decision, although I would have desired otherwise. Our brother Samuel plans to be with us, however," he added, his face brightening.

"How I have wished for Brother Samuel!" said Gabriel. "His knowledge of medicine and of surgery will be invaluable to us. For some weeks I had with me here an Indian, Joseph by name, who had brought his wife in the hope that I could cure her of an illness. It so happened that I could help her, and in gratitude Joseph showed me the best deer ranges and his squaw ground my corn."

"The Indians, then, are friendly?" queried Israel.

"Most of them respond to friendly gestures," said Gabriel, "but there are hostile Indians in the neighborhood."

"There is still work for us then," commented Israel.

"In the main, there is peace," explained Gabriel. "There is so much to do! My first crop of vegetables was very scant. There was no grain. My cabin and the shed where I store my furs and pelts

I built before the first frosts. I hunted deer and elk until the deep snows bound me in the cabin. I constructed my own furniture, rude as it is, and," he smiled as he took from a shelf a half-finished stocking, "you see what I do with my idle moments." He began to knit.

Johann tossed a knot of wood on the fire, and the talk went on. Gabriel had seen an occasional trapper or an Indian, but aside from these rare visitors life in the valley had been serene and undisturbed.

Israel looked about him. The cabin was large, substantial, and warm. From the rafters hung haunches of smoked venison and flitches of bear meat. Chunks of homemade soap were stacked on a ledge in the far corner. In a near corner stood an almost empty keg of powder. In another lay a pile of deerskins, half cured, and several shaggy bearskins.

"There is my work," said Gabriel. "Those skins will bring us a good fifty pounds."

"We have brought you some comforts," and Israel opened a canvas bag from his pack. "Here is an inkhorn, a sandglass, and a new stock of paper and ink. In another place we have hackles for flax and some scutching knives. We shall make ourselves a loom, and when Brother Samuel comes we can weave cloth. I have seeds. I have fishhooks. Our life should be filled with peace."

Heavy bearskins were piled on the floor, and on these the men lay down to sleep.

The following day the men began the building of the new cabin. The sheds were repaired so that they would be ready for the new skins and furs to be brought in. A garden was planted. A new cornfield was laid out. Each day had its work. Israel had organized the group and each of the four had his allotted tasks.

The brothers lodged together, while Daniel and Johann lived in a new cabin.

Israel set out his books on a shelf by his bedside. They were holy books: volumes of sermons, his Bible, treatises on the essence of God, examinations into the nature of sin and of the spirit. Israel spent long hours at his table reading, meditating, wrapt in pious thought, the outer world forgotten. At regular hours during the day and night he devoted himself to prayer.

When Gabriel went hunting for deer or turkeys, Israel worked in the garden or the new cornfield and went fishing with Johann.

Once Gabriel and Johann made a trip to Winchester, Virginia, for sheep. They also brought back with them two cows. A byre and a sheep pen were built. There would be milk and butter, and wool to weave.

As the summer heightened and waned the cabbages and lentils planted beside the creek matured. The corn rose, sturdy and full eared, in the field beyond the cabins. The hay in the little strip of meadow was yellowed and was cut and stacked in cocks.

One day Joseph, the Indian, came for some liniment such as Gabriel had given him the winter before.

"French soldiers are coming down from the north," he said. "They will take our valley from us unless the English build a strong house at the great forks of the rivers."

The brothers, safe in their little settlement, far from civilization and man-made wars, hardly believed that the peaceful world they had made for themselves could be threatened by invasion. Soon they forgot about the French, for in the autumn the third of the brothers arrived to make his home with them.

Samuel brought with him three horses, new linen shirts for Israel, stout brogues for all of them, and leather aprons for

Daniel and Johann. He brought a store of tea, white flour, boxes of rice, spices, a quantity of chocolate, and a set of account books. But beside all these, Samuel brought his silver flute.

In Ephrata the Sister House and the Brother House had rung with the sound of voices and instruments in heavenly music lasting hour after hour, until it was a wonder to the world to hear. Now there was strange and beautiful music in the Monongahela wilderness. Samuel had brought two books of music, hand-lettered and scored at Ephrata. His flute gave the music a light and mysterious quality in harmony with the religious spirit.

So life in the frontier valley moved in slow serenity. The sowing and the harvest, the fishing, the hunting, the daily prayers, the spiritual counsel—all passed in peace.

There was a third cabin in the wilderness. There were two more servants. There were twenty horses and a new horse mill. There was a tanning vat, and the pelts and furs were cured, bound into bales, and carried by pack horse over the mountains to Winchester, Virginia.

Samuel was the trader. He went unmolested on his trips. The Indians knew him as "Doctor Eckerlin," for he was often called upon to minister to his Indian neighbors in times of illness. The Indians were grateful and sent warnings to the brothers when danger threatened. They could never understand the brothers' indifference to these warnings. They could not know that these strange brothers lived in absolute faith—faith in divine protection, in divine love.

As the time drew near for Samuel's fall trading trip to Winchester he grew restless. The harvest was in, there was an autumn haze over the valley, and a breeze from the forest brought the scent of pine and leaf mold. It was time to set out again.

"Are the skins ready? Johann! Bring up the horses and pack-saddles! I am anxious to be off!" he called.

"Brother," said Gabriel, "there may be danger. Indian Joe has warned us of trouble at the forks."

"Even the hostile Indians know us, brother," said Samuel. "There is nothing to fear."

He and Johann were ready to start. The horses were fastened by ropes, the bales of furs lashed to the saddles. The provisions for the journey—blankets, powder, flour and meal, a griddle, an iron pot, some dried venison—all were ready.

In buckskin shirts and fringed leggings, Samuel and Johann mounted their horses. The white-circled tails of their coonskin caps dangled against their shoulders. Their powder horns swung at their sides. They turned south, keeping the trail that the Indians used, following the river, cutting through the valleys and around the mountains, bearing east. At night they spread their blankets before the fire and slept.

As he traveled Samuel's eye quickly noted and identified landmarks. Here was the sharp descent that led to a low river bank. Here was the place to ford the river. There was the giant boulder lodged against the hillside, and farther on the path swerved abruptly to the right to avoid a deep gully. A bad place, thought Samuel, but no one would bother to change the trail.

They met no one. Once a startled deer bounded across the path and Samuel brought it down with a quick shot. Fresh meat would be a welcome change from the dried venison they had brought along.

The two men were glad when they reached Winchester, for the journey was long and tedious. The trading concluded, they lost no time in starting back along the trail. Samuel's spirits rose.

He would be home in ten days or so. The horses would go faster now that their heavy burdens were gone.

At Port Pleasant they stopped to get provisions.

They met strange and hostile glances, and suddenly to his amazement Samuel was seized with rough hands.

"A spy! A spy!"

Samuel shook off the hands that held him.

"I am no spy," he said. "I am Samuel Eckerlin."

"Doctor Eckerlin, to the Indians. Oh yes, we know you, Doctor Eckerlin! You are a confederate of the Indians and of the French, and you are spying upon us."

In vain did Samuel protest his innocence. He was held at Port Pleasant while he tried every persuasion and every proof he knew.

"Let me write to the governor!" he cried at last.

It was not until Samuel's appeal to the governor of Virginia had been answered that he and Johann were permitted to start on their homeward journey, and then only with a squad of soldiers who were ordered to accompany them home.

Within a day's distance of his home, as Samuel rode over the hills with the soldiers, he looked down into a winding creek, and there his woods-trained eyes saw, crossing the shallow water below, a group of Indians. It was the first sight of any Indians he had had, and he did not want to meet them. Such a meeting might be mistaken for an assignation, agreed upon previously, and the soldiers might the more easily suspect him, then, of being a spy. He watched the Indians as they climbed the farther bank and disappeared into the forest. He sighed with relief. They were going the opposite way.

As Samuel helped to make camp he tried to shake off the disquieting doubts in his mind. He concentrated his thoughts upon

Israel and Gabriel waiting before the fire, eating supper perhaps, or talking quietly together. But when he slept he turned and muttered, and the figures of Indians dimly seen stalked through his dreams.

In the morning he forgot his bad night in the joy of reaching home, and he chafed at every small delay during the day. As they turned around the last low spur of hill, he felt his heart leap in anticipation.

"My home is in the next valley," Samuel told the soldiers.

They hastened on.

"Home! And peace," thought Samuel, and a lump came into his throat.

He passed through the forest gap into the clearing and looked out over the valley, a smile on his lips.

Then he stood as if frozen. The smile twisted in a horrible grimace. He was stunned. His eyes moved over the scene before him, and yet he did not see, would not see, the complete devastation before him.

Home.

Here was a mound of ashes. Here was a heap of charred logs. Home. Was this home?

"Israel!" Samuel cried. "Gabriel! My brothers! Oh, my brothers!"

He rushed forward. He was frantic with fear.

"Where are they? Where are they?"

Where were the cabins? Here? In these blackened heaps? Here had stood the brothers' house, here had stood the servants', and over here had stood the cook house. All, all were gone. The sheep and cows, killed and left where they fell, a dozen of them scattered over the clearing . . .

Samuel ran among them, sick with despair.

He found the bodies of Daniel and the two other servants. They had been scalped.

But his brothers? "Israel! Gabriel!"

There was no sign of them.

Johann and the soldiers dug shallow graves and buried the servants under stones, as well as they could in the gathering darkness. Above the ragged edge of tree tops showed the thin rim of the moon. Samuel looked up at the heavens and saw the bright star that marks the uplifted hand of Orion. Then the two stars of the shoulders appeared, and into the dark sky swung the great constellation. He caught his breath. He raised his arms to the fathomless night.

"Where, O Father, are my brothers?" he cried soundlessly, and his eyes dimmed with tears.

The night sky spread clear and sparkling over the head of the lone brother. He stumbled as he led his horse away.

It was said, years afterwards, that the two brothers were carried to France, where they died as prisoners.

It was said that the brothers died at sea.

It was said at Fort Duquesne that Gabriel had been taken there before being sent to Montreal and Quebec. Of Israel nothing was known.

But although one thing was said here, and another thing was told elsewhere, Samuel himself never found out what became of his brothers. All his life he searched for them. Over, and over, and over again he cried:

"Israel! Gabriel! Where are my brothers? My brothers, oh, my brothers!"

·[5]·

James Smith, Captive

ACROSS the wooded mountains an army was slowly moving. Along the trace that cut through the uncharted wilderness columns of soldiers were dragging brass artillery, ammunition, and provisions. Clattering, lumbering wagons, straining, clumping horses, drums, bugles, colors flying in the wind—the army of empire was moving, the army of Britain, brave with red coats and buff breeches, cocked hats and new muskets.

It was one of three British armies marching against the French posts. One was marching against Frontenac and Niagara. One was marching against Crown Point. And over the Allegheny Mountains to Fort Duquesne went the third—two thousand soldiers with heavy guns and cannon led by General Edward Braddock, Sir Peter Halkett, and Colonel Thomas Dunbar.

The army moved slowly. The large number of wagons in the train delayed its progress; crossing the mountains proved disastrous for the horses; rough roads retarded the foot soldiers, who had to stop to level hills and to build bridges over streams. Sometimes the army required as long as four days to cover twelve miles!

Spring passed and summer advanced while the army moved beyond the frontier. New, bright green needles spread along the pine branches. The maples sent out a golden green mist of young buds and leaves. Around the trunks of the trees and the gray mountain boulders laurel and rhododendron unfolded pink and magenta blossoms to brighten the brown earth and the dark shadows of the forest. The shadbush replaced its white flowers with ripening berries, and on all the dense branches the leaves opened and thickened. The broad-leaved wild grape fastened its thousand tendrils wherever it could. And beside the road, following the British army, marched an army of white and yellow daisies.

Fort Duquesne was still many miles away.

Fort Duquesne! Like a great irregular, five-pointed star fashioned of clay and logs it lay, lifted on a point of land above the three rivers and in the heart of a gigantic wilderness. Like a star, it lay beyond reach—the farthest outpost of empire. Three nations coveted that point: the French from the north, the British from the east, and the Indians from the north, west, and south.

For a year and three months the French captain had directed the construction of the fort. For a year and three months the French flag with its three white lilies had waved over Fort Duquesne. The French language was spoken. French names, long and formal and involved, were signed to letters, orders, and records: Pierre Claude de Picardy, seigneur de Contrecœur, captain and commandant of Fort Duquesne; Lionel de Beaujeu, captain of infantry; Lieutenant de Carqueville; Ensign de la Perade—names to be written into the history of a continent.

Indian names mingled with the French: Shingiss and Beaver, kings of the Delaware tribe, Chief Killbuck, conjuror and medicine man. The Indians, pushed from their rightful lands by both the British and the French, sold their strength now to one side and now to the other for what gain they could.

"We have taken up the hatchet for the French," said the Delawares. "Our French brothers have treated us well; they give us good gifts. We will strike the English. We will go on the warpath."

But they added among themselves, "As soon as the English are driven away, we will drive the French from the land also! We will have our own hunting grounds again!"

They moved freely in and out of the French fort as friends and allies. They saw the French militia come overland from the north by foot and on horseback, and French marines come down the winding Allegheny to moor their fleet of bateaux at the foot of the cliffs. French cadets arrived to lead the Indians in sallies against the English settlers, who persisted in their efforts to colonize the country, and against the few Germans who laboriously worked their way west. Now and then runaway Irish servants appeared at the fort, willing to accept any fate except the life of servitude.

Sometimes the Indians took their prisoners into the fort and tortured them on the parade ground. For the most part, however, they enacted such scenes of horror and torment at the edge of the forest, or on the island in the river, removed from the eyes and ears of the families living in the fort. The French feared that they would lose the support of their allies if they tried to prevent gantlet running and burnings at the stake. They agreed that the Indians should have the prisoners that were captured. Some, of course, were adopted into the tribes, to be treated as brothers. The French did not even interfere when a young British captive, Rachel, was forced to run the gantlet and was beaten unmercifully, scarred with blows from clubs and switches.

"Lucky it was no worse!" they said, for Rachel lived at the fort and latter married one of the French soldiers.

No, they did not interfere, even when the new captive, young James Smith, was flogged and beaten into insensibility. Why should they care about any Englishman?

But Captain Dumas, on an inspection tour of the guardhouse, looked at the boy and muttered, "The wretches!"

"Why you're nothing but a youngster," he said kindly. "How did you happen to be taken, lad?"

The tone of the voice reassured the prisoner. He had expected nothing but abuse and mistreatment, but here was an officer kindly disposed. He hesitated to answer questions about himself, however, and prudently decided to tell as little as he could.

"The Indians have already told you all I know," he explained finally. "We were cutting a road through the forest to Turkey Foot, and my companion and I were sent back to hurry up the provision wagons. Your Indians fired at us from the bushes, killing my friend outright. Me they missed. But my horse reared up and threw me, and before I could escape they had me."

"I do not hold with their ways," said Captain Dumas. "Your wounds will be washed with brandy. A doctor will see to you."

After he left the Indians came and stood over their prisoner menacingly.

"You better tell us how many English soldiers work in that road-making," they said.

"Three hundred English soldiers," said James Smith.

"Have they arms?" asked the Indians.

"Arms? Yes, they are very well armed!" said James Smith grimly.

He could truthfully answer that each of the three hundred soldiers had two strong arms, but he dare not tell the Indians that there were only about thirty guns in the whole force. The Indians would kill and scalp every man of them before morning! If he could give evasive answers, if he could manage to convey the impression that Colonel Burd's forces were formidably armed, perhaps he could discourage the Indians from attacking. Saving Colonel Burd's men might save General Braddock and his army, too.

"If I could only get word to them," he thought. "If I could only send them some information about this fort."

"Those Indians, the Iroquois, with the English—they quarrel, they fight," warned the Indians. "They deceived us. They will deceive the English! Never mind. You forget all that. You belong to us now. We will take care of you!"

They grinned hideously and left him.

The young prisoner groaned. Terror struck his heart. Were they planning more tortures? Would they give him death at the stake or doom him to life with their tribe? He had heard reports of some Indian adoptions. No, he must escape! He determined to seize the first opportunity to get away. He began to plan every possible means to evade his captors.

As his wounds healed, James Smith was allowed the freedom of the fort. He deliberately set about to win the good will and friendship of everyone he met. He knew how to ward off the hatred of the Indians and to put himself in their good graces. He knew enough of French and of the Indian languages to pick up a great deal of information. He could speak Dutch, and he found some old soldiers who talked to him in that language.

The fort to the landward of the rivers had been built of squared logs; that part facing the rivers, of stockades of round logs. Intrenchments had been cast up to a height of seven feet. Against these were thrown a very gradual ascent of earth. There were two gates, a magazine, a well, a kitchen, a smithy, a storehouse, and the house of the commandant. There were bark huts for the garrison. Outside the fortress was the parade ground, at the edge of which clustered the bark wigwams of the Delawares, whose squaws sat stringing wampum, grinding corn, or curing their tobacco.

The fort was well guarded. Escape seemed impossible.

Day by day the scouts and runners reported the progress of Braddock's army, the size of it, the steady, dauntless march forward, and the earnest persistence of the English soldiers.

"They use block and tackle to lower cannon and mortar from the sides of the mountains!" said the scouts. "They have almost superhuman powers."

James Smith listened to the reports with ill-concealed pride. But the Indians muttered among themselves. It was not reasonable to fight in this war! Let the French and the English fight among themselves. After all what would the Indians get out of it? They would just be pushed out of the land, west, and still farther west.

The French felt the Indians wavering in their loyalty. They decided to appear to ignore the oncoming army and tried to divert the Indians from their fears, arranging drills and parades to display the strength of the French forces, to assure the Indian allies of certain victory.

Under the lively, almost gay life of the fort there were, nevertheless, undercurrents of anxiety. Among the officers there were differences of opinion that were argued heatedly.

James Smith kept his eyes and his ears open.

"Captain de Contrecœur has decided to abandon the fort without a blow," whispered the French officers.

"Captain de Beaujeu insists upon preparing an ambuscade for the English!"

"One thousand French against four thousand English. That's destruction!"

James Smith smiled to himself. So Braddock was supposed to have four thousand men. He himself had helped to spread reports about the strength of the British army. If only the English captains could know how the facts had been exaggerated. Nothing could stop them! If he were only free! If he could only get word to Braddock!

"Captain de Contrecœur will dispute the passage of the Monongahela River but he will give up the fort without a blow." The rumor was persistent.

"Captain de Beaujeu is going to prepare an ambush on the banks of the Monongahela River." This rumor persisted also, and it was a rumor James Smith disliked. An ambush, and no way to warn the English! That meant certain disaster, a surprise attack and the advantage of cover. . . .

James Smith looked around cautiously. But he was too well watched: he could not escape. He had been put to work mending canoes on the high ground near the river. He melted some resin in a skillet and started to fill in a long crack in the bark. Two French marines and an Indian emerged from the woods along the Monongahela. The marines were carrying a stretcher improvised from two poles and a blanket.

"What is it?" he asked. "What has happened?"

"A French officer, shot by English army scouts," said the Indian. "Two Indians and a white man, they were. Gist maybe."

"Christopher Gist!" said James. "Did you—get them?"

"No," grunted the Indian. "All escaped. We shot after them. That white man might be Gist. Indians all know him."

James Smith rejoiced inwardly at the escape, but he said nothing. As he worked he thought, "If I'd only known Gist was that near I'd have made a dash for the woods! But what if I had tried that? Gist might have thought me a French spy. I might have been shot by my own people. No, it's hopeless. I'd be tracked by the Indians."

But he chafed in his captivity. If he could only warn Braddock!

Runners brought new information.

"Some British crossed the Monongahela ford. That means a change in Braddock's route."

"They are coming!"

"Coming? They're almost here!"

The captive clenched his hands to keep them from trembling. If Braddock could only know the uneasiness that followed this news. If he could only know that the officers were divided among themselves. That the French position was insecure. That the Indian allies were wavering and unstable. Already some of them had left the fort. If Braddock would only come with his army before Captain de Beaujeu carried out his plan of an ambush! The young captive gripped his hands until the knuckles hurt. It was so hard to stand there and do nothing. It was hard to know that the English were so near. He might be rescued from his captivity if they would strike quickly! He was conscious of the dull and heavy beating of his heart, scarcely aware of the hurried prepartions within the fort.

The first thing James noticed was that one of the guns had

been mounted on its carriage. This indicated that the fort was to be abandoned or else surrendered "with the honors of war." The thought of either outcome elated him.

But that night the fort was stormy with argument. The officers openly disputed Captain de Contrecœur's decision. Give up the fort? There was violent dissension. Captain de Beaujeu was tense and excited. He explained, with rigid determination, his plan for an ambush.

"An ambush!" scoffed Captain de Contrecœur. "The only effect of an ambush would be to annoy the English and defer their arrival at the fort!"

Captain Dumas answered thoughtfully and reasonably: "The force at the fort is small. It would be more effective if placed at a special point along the route, in a surprise attack. Here, at the fort, I doubt our ability to make a stand."

"And the Indians!" reminded Captain de Beaujeu. "Shingiss, Pontiac, and Killbuck will go with us if we lay an ambush. I have the word of King Shingiss!"

"But we fight alone if we fight within the fort?" asked Captain de Contrecœur.

"Shingiss says it is against Indian law and custom to join open battle with superior numbers!" explained De Beaujeu, smiling a little.

"The English cannon frighten them," growled one of the officers. "And they hate bayonets."

The men were evenly divided, some for surrender, some for ambuscade. The argument settled into a deadlock.

But the next morning Captain de Contrecœur suddenly agreed to the plan for an ambush.

The day was spent in hurried preparation. The Indian chiefs

and the French captains located the most favorable positions
for their surprise attack. All day the fort was a scene of great
activity. One hundred marines, a score of cadets, a hundred Canadians, and six hundred Indians filled the court. They came and
went between the smithy, the storehouse, and the bark huts of
the garrison. The Indians streaked their faces with fresh vermilion, and helped themselves liberally to bullets, powder, and
flints from the barrels that were rolled out of the stores. They
were well pleased with the plans of Captain de Beaujeu. French
brandy put them in high spirits and they made the night terrifying with war whoops.

At dawn, while the mists still clung to the high banks along
the river, before reveille was sounded and the fort began to stir,
Captain de Beaujeu went to confession in the chapel of the
Assumption of the Blessed Virgin, bowed before Father Denys
Baron, and prepared himself for death.

"What you do this day, you will do for God and for France,"
said the priest.

The captain rose from his knees and buckled on his sword.

"For God and France!" he said.

The yard was lively and noisy with Indians and soldiers making
hasty last-minute preparations for departure. Officers hurried
from guardroom to barracks, from bastion to storehouse, from
smithy to magazine. James Smith, climbing to the ramparts,
watched the scene within and without, speaking occasionally to
the sentinels, his heart like a stone, his thoughts bitter. He heard
farewells spoken, but he took no part in them. He saw the officers
holding hurried consultations, and heard them give terse instructions. A sharp command was called. The soldiers formed
ranks, as the Indians moved away from the fort in single file.

The French columns followed across the parade ground and off through the woods.

An unnatural quiet fell within the fort. The yard was deserted. The wind from the river stirred the dust, and from a rampart James Smith could hear the lapping of the water against the sand and pebbles of the steep bank.

Somehow the silence was harder to bear than the noise of the soldiers. The captive grew restless. All his thoughts were with Braddock and the English army.

"If only I might have warned them," he thought again and again.

Morning slowly dragged along. Noon passed, and he ate the scanty meal without appetite. The afternoon sun was high, but there was no news.

Elderly men idled about the fort cleaning guns, sharpening knives, and mending moccasins. Women took their sewing into the yard and sat in the shade of the westernmost bastion. Their flying fingers disclosed the nervous strain of waiting. Children clambered aimlessly over the ramparts and walls. The air seemed heavy with suspense.

"What is happening? What are they doing?" exploded James. He waited tensely for the first sight of a runner with news.

Suddenly an Indian sped from the woods towards the fort.

James leaped from the ramparts to meet him.

"Beaujeu!" gasped the Indian. "Beaujeu is killed! The British have cannon. My people ran away; they do not like cannon."

"Who has taken command?"

"Captain Dumas."

The men and women ran forward to hear the news.

"What will happen now?" they asked, gathering into groups

to discuss the disaster. Perhaps more men were needed? Troops were called and ordered to march.

Another runner, a white scout, came in breathlessly.

"We met them climbing the second hill from the river. Their cannons frightened the Indians, and hordes of them ran away. Captain de Beaujeu fell at the first fire."

"Oh, oh!" groaned the women, "what will they do?"

"They have rallied," continued the scout. "They are flanking the British on both sides of the column."

Their faces brightened. That sounded more hopeful.

James Smith turned away.

One after another, scouts and runners appeared. Almost before one had delivered his report, another came to add to it.

"We have stopped them! Then English charged up the hill with bayonets. You know how the Indians hate bayonets. But they have concealed themselves perfectly. The British soldiers cannot see them, and so they fire only when they see the smoke from the Indian's rifles."

The French soldiers laughed. That was funny to them. They gave no thought to the young English captive whose hands clenched and unclenched, and whose eyes shone with anger.

"They are panic-striken, those English!" came the exultant cry from the French.

"They are firing at random. They don't know what they are doing. We shall surely have them before night."

"One of the leaders has been hurt. Maybe Braddock himself!"

"Hundreds have been killed. They lie thick in the woods. They are fighting so closely that their bullets strike their own men."

"Oh, it's a slaughter, horrible to see!"

"Already five hundred of them are dead. They are firing among

"Arms? Yes, they are very well armed!" said James Smith grimly.

themselves in a panic. They don't know how or where to shoot; they just keep firing blindly, crazed and confused."

James Smith listened, sick at heart. His eyes glistened with unshed tears; something tight and hard gripped his throat. If he closed his eyes he could see the riot and disorder in the English ranks. The English soldiers would be completely bewildered. The soldiers from Virginia, accustomed to fighting the Indians, would want to fight as the Indians were fighting—behind bushes and trees. But Braddock, whose discipline and formal army tactics were his very breath, would insist upon keeping the men in ranks even in the thickest forest. He would think the Virginians a cowardly lot of soldiers, getting behind trees to fight!

Young Colonel George Washington knew the Indians, and he knew that they must be met with their own war methods, not with stiff and formal European drill measures. But Washington was not in command. He had to take orders, not give them.

"Braddock is trying to rally the men," came the next report, "but they will no longer listen to him! It's a sight to see: Braddock trying to form platoons, trying to keep rank, trying to charge an unseen enemy."

"Why he must be crazy!" said the soldiers in the fort. "But it's lucky for us that he is a fool."

"The Indians pick off the officers—they are so easily seen— and that adds to their confusion."

"Two more officers are wounded, and Halkett has been killed!"

"There's one thing I must say," said one of the scouts, earnestly; "laugh as you will, Braddock is a soldier. Four horses have been shot and killed under him. He is always in the center of the fighting. His officers are falling all around him, and it's no easy job he has. He has courage."

"Washington has had two horses shot under him," reported another. "He is tall and makes a good target. He has been shot at so frequently that the Indians think he is charmed. They will not waste their bullets on him any more!"

"When his men deserted their cannon, he leaped from his horse and with his own hands pointed the brass fieldpiece toward the woods. I myself saw him."

"Bullets have cut his coat, of that I am certain," declared a young Indian. "Yes, it is true, he possesses some charm to keep him safe from our bullets."

The heart of the listening prisoner leaped with pride. Washington! He was only a few years older than himself. But what courage! What fearlessness!

Another scout staggered into the fort, spent with excitement.

"Braddock has fallen. I saw with my own eyes how he was struck and fell from his horse."

"Killed?" The French soldiers leaned forward eagerly.

"He was carried off," said the scout. "Furthermore, the whole army has been completely routed."

"The river was their only retreat!"

"Oh, how they ran!"

"All abandoned! Horses, cattle, wagons, guns—everything! They rushed to the ford, and the Indians followed them down to the river—scalping, of course."

Firing their guns and yelling in triumph, the French soldiers straggled back to the fort.

"All over but collecting the spoils," they reported.

From the woods came a score of Indians giving their scalp halloos, accompanied by a number of French soldiers, all bearing the sinister marks of war: dust, and blood, and powder stains, and grimy makeshift bandages. From the Indians' belts hung bloody scalps. The French had prizes they had picked up: caps of the British grenadiers, British canteens, knives, bayonets dark with blood, gold chains and other bits of jewelry, and even British coins. Food and ammunition were brought back on horseback.

As the last of the soldiers returned from the woods a mighty shout went up, and the great guns of Fort Duquesne boomed victory!

James Smith left the ramparts and went to his quarters un-noticed. Sounds of rejoicing and merrymaking filled the air. From the fort yard outside came the hideous din of Indian war whoops and scalp halloos and of the booming guns on the bastion. In the sky to the north a red glow revealed an Indian camp where prisoners of war were being tortured and burned at the stake. James shuddered and threw himself on his bunk.

A soldier entered and flung a small book down beside him.

"From the battlefield," he said. "It's English. Do you want it?"

James looked up. He held the book in hands that were still unsteady.

"What is it?" asked the soldier.

"Russel's *Seven Sermons*," James answered.

"Sermons!" The Frenchman shrugged and turned away.

James Smith held the book in his hands, idly turning over its pages. It would be good to have an English book to read. Having the book would be almost like having a friend. Nine miles away, in the ravine across the river, lay hundreds of British soldiers, dead and dying. The green leaves of the laurel which that morn-ing had gleamed through the sunny mist were cut and broken and trampled to the ground. English blood spattered the earth.

English hopes were shattered. . . . Would those hopes revive?
Would an English army march again through the Ohio Valley
against this fort at the three rivers?

Day after day James Smith thought of the future and found it
dark and unfathomable. He had no more hope of being rescued.
He had no hope of escape. He was lonely and despondent. Even
death at the torture stake would be a welcome alternative to life
as an Indian captive.

"Tecangretanego will adopt you as his son," the Indians told
him, and the words repeated themselves in his mind like a sen-
tence of doom, over and over again.

Tecangretanego. Who was he? Just another savage, cruel and
terrifying, James thought indifferently.

There was a knock, firm and insistent, and in the doorway
stood a noble and dignified chief.

Involuntarily, James stood up before him. Just another savage? No, the first glance revealed the greatness of the man. The
white youth's eyes looked searchingly into that proud face.

"What do you want?" he asked.

"Come, my son," said Tecangretanego.

·[6]·

Scoouwa the White Brother

"YOHOH-YOHOH! Yohoh-Yohoh!"

The call sounded through the long valley, echoed and re-echoed in the early hours of the autumn morning, and startled into sudden wakefulness the young English captive in the Indian camp.

"Yohoh-yohoh!"

The weird call made him shiver. Instinctively he thrust out a hand for his rifle, and then he remembered that he had none; remembered the ordeal of his adoption into the Indian tribe as the son of the chief, Tecangretanego; remembered that he was no longer James Smith, Pennsylvanian, but Scoouwa, brother to these Delawares with painted skins and alien ways.

"Yohoh-yohoh!"

He held his breath and leaned forward, listening.

He recognized that Indian call. It meant that the Indian council had decided to cross Lake Erie and continue the journey, even if the lake waters were storm-tossed and fiercely raging. That call was like a command and a question together; it must be answered. The rest of the tribe must be in agreement with the council, or the decision of the council would be dropped.

"Ooh-ooh!" There it was—the answer!

James sat up, hugging his knees.

"So!" he said to himself. "Then it is agreed. They will go then, even if the lake is seething! 'Agreed,' they answered. 'The lake shall be crossed, if the council so wills it.' Well! There is nothing I can do. I must go where they go . . . "

He flung his blanket over his shoulder and walked to the edge of the lake, letting his eyes travel out over the western waters. Surely, he thought, no frail canoe could withstand the force of those beating waves, the strain and swell of that distant unknown whirlpool!

"You go?" he asked Tontileaugo, his Indian brother. He knew it was an idle question, for Tontileaugo was directing the loading of the canoes and scarcely paused to nod an assent. James watched this man with an interest touched with respect, and suddenly felt confidence in the safe travel of the canoes across the lake. Tontileaugo, if he sensed the danger at all, seemed to ignore it, to put it aside as of little importance.

All the Indians, James noticed, glanced at the lake indifferently. The water was rough, the way would be difficult—but what of that? Other waters had been rough; other sailings had been hazardous. Hand to hand and shoulder to shoulder they could brave the heaviest sea. The Lake Spirit troubled the waters and might retard their progress and exhaust their strength; nevertheless they would press forward. It was agreed.

Many times during the hazardous crossing of the lake James Smith marveled at the skill of his red brothers, and at their powers of endurance as the long day dragged on. To him the trip was one of intense strain, even of terror. It seemed endless, and yet when the final landing-place was reached without serious mishap, the Indians set about making their camp in the most

matter-of-fact way. Just as if, thought James, the whole thing
had not been truly miraculous!

In spite of his persistent and wholehearted dislike of his new
brothers, Scoouwa, the white brother, found growing in himself a certain respect for them which he was reluctant to admit.
He grudgingly acknowledged to himself the fine qualities of
Tontileaugo, his brother by adoption, and it came to him
suddenly that, in order to keep on hating these red men, he had
to remember the first days of his capture so many weeks ago . . .
the surprise attack . . . the killing of Arnold Vigoras, his companion . . . the stumbling of his horse . . . his own escape from
death . . .

"As long as I live," thought James, "I'll always wonder why the
Indians spared my life!"

He thought again of the long forced run through the woods—
fifteen miles—and a cold night on the mountain when, bruised
and exhausted, he waited, even hoped, for death.

"And plenty of times I've wished they had killed me that
night," thought James bitterly, remembering the cruel tortures
that he had experienced.

Fifty miles farther through rocky laurel thickets they had
trudged to reach the Loyalhanna, and on the west side of Laurel
Hill, in sight of the Indian encampment, his captors had given
the scalp halloo for the scalps they had, and for their prisoner.

"I can still hear how they shrieked and shouted, and the guns
they fired. And I thought they would surely kill me!" James shook
his head in a puzzled way. "Then they gave me a feast of venison
and turkey—fed me as well and as generously as they fed their
brothers!"

He knew now, after weeks of Indian life, that this was the

way of the Indians. They shared their food to the last bite, the last crumb. The poor and scanty fare of mouldy biscuits and bits of roasted ground hog along the trail to the camp had been painstakingly divided into equal amounts.

"They are fair, and generous," James decided, hesitatingly, however, for the next instant, recalling his experiences, his eyes grew dark with anger.

Running the gantlet!

"Just an old Indian custom," they had said!

James wanted to forget that ordeal: the painted Indians running to meet him, *with clubs!* Red, black, brown, and blue—a maze of weird figures beating him as he staggered through the lines, knocked like a ball from one to the other until he fell to the ground, senseless.

Just an old Indian custom: running the gantlet!

"I remember wishing them to strike the fatal blow—they were too long about it," thought James.

He pondered again over his days at Fort Duquesne, his anxiety about Braddock's army, his grief at the news of Braddock's defeat . . . Again he could hate the Indians for their part in that encounter. He was English!

He felt in his blanket for his books: the book of English sermons a French soldier had brought from that bloody battleground and thrown carelessly on the bed, and an English Bible given to him by a kindly Dutch woman before he had left home. It was wonderful enough to have these books of his own to read, but here in this wild country, away from his own people, they became priceless treasures. They were, except for his bowl and spoon, his blanket and his scant clothing, his only possessions; they were his only friends. The Indians, strangely enough, regarded them as something living and stood in awe of them.

"The books speak to our brother," they said mystified, "but they do not speak to us. It is the white man's spirit, perhaps, living there," and they were afraid to destroy the volumes, fearing that the wrath of the book spirits would descend upon them.

Nevertheless, as James read the books and pondered over them, he felt the eyes of the Indians on him, watching him without seeming to do so, warily, guardedly, as if the books might prove to be dangerous . . .

Left behind in camp while the Indians hunted for deer and raccoons, James found comfort in reading, and in his leisure made a leather pouch for his precious volumes, against the dampness of the autumn air.

It was on his return from gathering chestnuts one day three miles up the river from the camp at Canesadooharie that he realized the books were missing! He searched the camp. He could not believe he had lost them himself. He suspected they had been stolen.

"Maybe the puppies carried them off," volunteered the Indians, sympathetically.

James suspected that the Indians themselves, displeased at his reading, had destroyed them or hidden them. He quietly continued his search, but the books were gone. His resentment against the Indians grew more bitter.

But the Indians had other and more important things to think about. The large canoe must be buried in the ground to preserve it during the months of heavy snow, a frame must be erected and the skins they had must be hung there, out of reach of any prowling wolves, to stay through the winter until the hunters came again. Twenty-two miles away was the place Tontileaugo had chosen for the winter camp of the group that followed him, and the first flurries of snow hurried them on. A long low cabin, built of cut logs, was finished in December. It was fifteen feet long and four feet high; at the top was an open place to serve as a chimney, and on the ground, bark, on which to put bearskins for their beds.

Food became scarce. The woods yielded nothing but a few hickory nuts. It was too late for red haws. The animals seemed to have been frightened away. Two small turkeys were scant fare for eight hunters and thirteen squaws and boys, everyone receiving an equal amount. Hard times were upon them. Hunger was the common fate of all.

Tontileaugo took James twelve miles away to hunt for bears.

"See bear tracks on tree trunk," explained Tontileaugo, and James saw where the tree had been scratched by the climbing bear looking for a hole high up in the trunk where he might sleep for the winter. James forced the bears out of their hiding holes, sometimes with the aid of a burning brand, sometimes by cutting down the hollow tree, and Tontileaugo, waiting with bent bow, drove his blunt-headed arrows into them as they emerged snuffing the air, disturbed and uncertain.

"Come, eat hearty; we have meat in plenty now," said Tontileaugo as he roasted some of the bear meat over the fire.

James found it hard to eat; he had not had meat for days. In the rude shelter of bark that was their camp he wrapped himself in his blanket and sat crosslegged before the fire. Now he might read, if only he had his books. He did not know the Indian language well enough to talk very much to Tontileaugo, and the Indian had the same difficulty with English. James found the days long. The hunting afforded him little pleasure, for he was allowed only a bow and arrow, and he remembered with shame the restrictions put upon him.

One day he had been given a gun and told to take the dogs down the creek and kill turkeys, but he had been lured over the hills by buffalo tracks, farther and farther from camp. At sundown he had found he could not follow his own tracks back to camp. Darkness had fallen. Fog and mist had confused him. He had tried to shout, but his voice had mocked him in the echo from the opposite hill.

"Coo-wigh! Coo-wigh!" he had called, remembering how the Indians gave their alarm halloo.

"Coo-wigh! Coo-wigh!" his own voice had answered him.

All night he had lain huddled against a tree trunk.

In the morning the Indians, following his tracks, had found and directed him back to the camp, scolding him because he had disobeyed their orders.

"Did you think I was running away?" James had asked.

"No, no!" they had laughed, "you go much too crooked!"

Nevertheless, the gun they had given him for hunting was taken away, and now he had only a bow and arrow. He was warned: "Watch tracks. Maybe buffalo tracks, maybe our enemies, the Catawba." It was Mohawk Solomon, the hunter who cautioned him.

James looked puzzled and incredulous.

"Surely they were buffalo tracks!" he exclaimed.

"Hush, you know nothing. Catawba bad Indians. Pass camp with buffalo hoofs on feet to make false tracks. False buffalo tracks lead good Indians away from camp into ambush. Catawba kill many Indians this way. So you watch buffalo tracks."

Little by little James learned from the Indians their way of living, and found that it was good. Tontileaugo taught him to be a skillful hunter. Bears, turkeys, racoons, and deer—the supply increased day by day until the two men could not carry it back to the encampment unaided. They packed what they could on their backs, then brought men and boys from the camp to help.

As winter passed and the sap rose in the maples the squaws made elm bark vessels and tapped the trees. They made great troughs to hold the sugar water—large enough to hold one hundred gallons of the sweet sap—and then they boiled the sap down to a syrup, poured it into molds to harden, and set the sugar cakes aside for use during the rest of the year.

From the bears the hunters brought in the squaws saved the fat. After the fat had been fried down, the oil was used in many ways. Vension was dipped in it. Sweetened with sugar, it was a syrup for coarse bread. Often the Indians smeared themselves with bear oil until their bodies glistened.

While the women went about their tasks, the men set traps for raccoons, foxes, wildcats, and other animals, for fur pelts, for provisions for the camp. When the time came to return to the camp at Canesadooharie, the large canoe was not sufficient to carry the supply of sugar and oil and skins, so an elm bark canoe was constructed to take care of the surplus. It had been a good winter, after all.

"Scoouwa!" a young Wyandot waved his arms as the bark canoe was brought in to land.

"Scoouwa!" shouted the Indians.

They looked at James with smiles and grimaces, trying to show their joy.

"The books! The books!" they shouted.

"Our brother was grieved to lose his books. Now they are

found. We rejoice that the books are found!" they said, crowding around James, as if the loss had been theirs and the restoration theirs also.

James held the books in both hands, hardly able to believe his good luck. Perhaps the bindings were damaged a little. But that did not make the books less precious. James looked at the friendly faces around him and was touched by the simple un-selfish joy they exhibited. He had suspected them of stealing!

Suddenly his heart warmed to these Indians, his brothers.

"I rejoice, and I thank my brothers for my books, and for the kindness my brothers show me," said James. He placed his hand on the forearm of the Indian who had found the lost volumes.

"Good!" said the Indians, and returned to their work with satisfaction.

Each month brought its particular tasks to the camp, but Tontileaugo was restless. He was a hunter, and he wanted to feel his gun in his hand, his bow and arrows against his back, he wanted to feel the soft black earth of the forest under his moccasins, he wanted to hear the crackling of twigs and the startling, sudden rush of the game he was hunting.

On the first day of April Tontileaugo took James hunting thirty miles up the river. Bears and raccoons and beavers were plentiful. A stray horse, mare, and colt running wild stirred Tontileaugo to a high pitch of excitement.

"We soon run them down!" he said to James.

"I don't believe we can do it," said James doubtfully.

"Tontileaugo can do it. Bears, buffaloes, and elk are not as swift as Tontileaugo, and in the great plains a deer is not as swift. In a whole day I can tire or run down any four-footed animal, except a wolf," boasted the hunter.

"But even a wolf will tire before a horse," said James, still skeptical.

"Tontileaugo will try this thing." He looked at James with half-closed eyes. "I heard the Wyandot say my brother runs well—now I shall see whether it is so."

James could run seven or eight miles at a time, but to an Indian that was nothing. To catch those wild horses it might be necessary to run all day!

Early in the morning the chase began, but after five hours James lagged behind and lost sight of Tontileaugo and the horses.

"Horses are wonderfully strong to run," he said to himself resignedly.

He passed the noon hours in a vain search for the runners, but at midafternoon the horses came racing by him, and he closed in after them. At sundown, however, the horses were lost to sight, and the hunters returned to their camp. James felt the hard running had been futile, but the Indian was pleased.

"We tired them," Tontileaugo insisted.

The Indian was right. The weary horses were captured the next day, and the work of training them for use was begun. With the horses, transporting the furs from the camp to the Indian town was much easier. The French traders bought all the skins and furs the hunters could bring in from the forest, and the Indians traded the pelts for new clothes, new paint, and tobacco.

In June and July the Indians spent their time in dancing and singing, playing games, feasting, smoking, and idling through the summer days. James thought his Indian brothers lived together in greater peace and harmony, love and friendship, than his English brothers. He never heard the Indians curse or swear.

They did not steal from one another. Their wrongs were righted in a common council. They were under obligations to love and defend one another and they shared the common tasks without complaint, knowing that they shared the benefits after the work was over.

In October came geese, swans, ducks, and cranes from the north, and the Indians had new meat to eat.

And one day Tecangretanego arrived and asked James to hunt with him on Cuyahoga—Tecangretanego, the head of the family, the greatest hunter of them all.

"Let me consider this," said James, for he wanted to talk to Tontileaugo.

"You have been as a brother to me," he said, "but now Tecangretanego, my older brother, my father, has come and asked me to hunt with him."

Tontileaugo puffed thoughtfully on his pipe.

"Tecangretanego is chief, and a better man than I am. You will do well. Do as you choose."

"I am attached to brother Tontileaugo," explained James, "but I am pleased with my old father's conduct and conversation, and I will see a part of the country I have never been in."

"It is well." Tontileaugo dismissed the matter, and James looked forward to new hunting, for Tecangretanego wanted beavers.

The hunting party accordingly followed Beaver River, then turned inland to a pond and found the beavers "more plentiful than ever." Tecangretanego marveled at this.

"Every year," he told James, "all beavers here are killed, yet next winter they come again, more plentiful! Beavers do not travel by land, and have no way out of pond. How is it that such numbers of beavers can get here year after year?"

James laughed.

"I suppose they have secret breeding places," he suggested.

"No," declared Tecangretanego, seriously. "Geese come from north in large numbers and turn into beavers—all but feet, which stay the same." He showed James the feet of the beavers, webbed like the feet of the geese.

James knew the Indians had strange ideas and superstitions, but he was surprised that Tecangretanego, who was exceptionally intelligent, should believe such a story. He was even more surprised to hear that when the winter traps set for raccoons were found in the spring to have rattlesnakes in them, the Indians believed that the raccoons had turned into rattlesnakes. In winter the rattlesnakes would turn back again into raccoons, they said.

James could laugh at these stories; it made no difference to the Indians. In turn they laughed at his ignorance of forest life.

James learned to know the tracks of animals, and when snow fell it was a simple matter for him to follow squirrels and rabbits and raccoons, while the Indians hunted beavers in the frozen ponds, breaking the hollow ice, and catching the animals by their hind legs. Snow fell heavily. James persistently followed the maze of tracks and one day was excited to find a family of raccoons. He stopped and hallooed for the Indians, but there was no reply. Again and again he called. He was disappointed that he must leave the raccoons, but he could not get them without help, so he reluctantly turned back. He followed his own tracks, but the snow had filled up the impressions until he could scarcely find the way. Soon he lost the tracks entirely, found them again only to flounder from one tree to another, looking for familiar landmarks.

"Surely this is the hickory tree I passed," he thought. "Surely this is the direction, to the left, to the camp."

He went on, stumbling over hidden roots, dropping into unexpected holes, stopping to look about him, giving the alarm halloo.

"Coo-wigh! Coo-wigh!"

Only the soft falling of snow and his own breathing disturbed the silence.

He leaned against a fallen tree and tried to think what he might do. He must build himself some sort of shelter, he decided, and looking about him he spied a hollow tree with a hole at one side.

"Three feet wide and plenty high," he thought.

He chopped and carried wood until he had built up a wall three or four feet high, all around the opening, leaving only the smallest hole to creep in, and a block to haul in after him. He made a bed of the dry wood inside the tree, stripped off his moccasins and danced to warm his frozen feet, then curled himself up in his blanket, and in the darkness of his den, slept through the long night.

When he opened his eyes, he saw nothing but blackness. He groped his way to the block in the opening, but he could not move it.

"Perhaps I have slept only a few hours," he thought, and he wrapped his blanket around him. "It is dark because it is still night."

Again he slept. Again he opened his eyes to darkness. He tried the block and could not move it.

"A great snow has blocked me in," he thought, and terror seized him. "I have buried myself alive!"

He exerted all his strength against the entrance block.

"Light! If I could only see light!"

He threw himself against the block. He gathered all his force and strength and strained every muscle in a supreme effort.

The block moved!

A light shower of snow fell into the darkness of the den.

"Light!" he cried, laughing and crying. "Once more, light of heaven!"

Panting from his efforts, he forced himself to keep pushing against the block and at last he could manage to crawl out of his black den and stand blinking in the white snow light.

What direction should he take?

He looked at the trees around him, and then he remembered what Tontileaugo had told him long ago.

"Moss always grows on the northwest side of trees."

He hurriedly examined the trees, and guided by the mossy sides of them he found his way with difficulty to the creek. At this point he was less than a mile from the camp.

With shouts of joy the Indians welcomed him.

"We would have gone for you," they cried. "See! We have made snowshoes for fast travel over the snow. We rejoice that our brother lives and returns to us!"

Tecangretanego placed a hand on his shoulder.

"We are glad to see you on your own account," he said sincerely, "and we are glad to see the prospect of your filling the place of a great man in whose place you were adopted. You have given evidence of your fortitude, skill, and resolution, and we hope you will always go on to do great actions, as it is only great actions that can make a great man."

This was high praise from Tecangretanego. James was embarrassed, for he thought, "it was no great action to try to save my own life." He remembered his moments of terror with a feeling of guilt and shame. An Indian boy would have been more brave. Nevertheless the words of praise were kind and his heart warmed to his Indian father.

The months that followed were occupied with hunting, fighting, trapping, and trading in the Indian towns, just the same as the year before. The squaws made sugar. The summer months were given over to games. Some of the Indians prepared to go to war against the frontier settlers, but in the council Tecangretanego bitterly opposed violence.

"Let the English and the French fight their own battles," he insisted. "They have contrived this war to waste the Indians and divide the land between them. Our land! Did not the Great Spirit give us our land? Why do these white men drive us away from our own places?"

But some of the Indians spoke against the words of the chief.

"We have taken up the hatchet for Onontio, the French governor, brother. These French have always treated us well, and the Great Spirit will go with us."

"English or French, it is all the same," declared Tecangretanego. "And we are but a handful against them."

He was distressed when the warriors left camp and returned again with horses and plunder, and, often enough, scalps and prisoners.

The hunting month found James alone with Tecangretanego and the young son of Tontileaugo. The old chief was lame with rheumatism, and James found it more and more difficult as winter passed to provide food for them. Several days passed without the least success in hunting.

"Not even a squirrel," he grumbled. "Where have they gone?
Are they all dead?"

"When the squirrel dies the nuts he has planted grow into
trees," said the young boy. "So if the squirrels have died we will
have a forest of nut trees."

James turned away. Idle superstitions. Idle talk. He grew
more and more discouraged and despondent.

"Why do I stay here?" he wondered. "Hostile Indians are
everywhere, it is true, and if I try to escape they would just capture me again and make me prisoner. Here I am starving. What
difference whether I die at the hands of enemy Indians, or of
starvation?"

He sat by the fire, brooding.

In the morning he took his gun and his blanket and left the
camp without a word.

He walked on and on, weak from hunger, not knowing what
trail he took and not caring. Half consciously, James went on
farther, mile after mile, without any feeling of exhaustion, on
and on, away from the old chief and the boy in the camp. Sometimes, in desperation, he ran with short unsteady steps. He
thought of nothing. His mind seemed blank. His eyes searched
the ground, and yet he saw nothing. He did not notice the regular marks sharply indented in the soft earth.

He followed the tracks instinctively. Suddenly he saw them for
what they were. He came to life. Buffalo tracks! In a frenzy of
haste he followed them. Buffalo meat! The thought of food
became overpowering. When he spied the buffalo his hands
trembled, but he killed the beast and tasted his first meat in
many days.

"Now," he thought exultantly. "I am strong! I can go on in

the moonlight many miles. I can escape and find my way back to my own people!"

He cut off as much of the buffalo meat as he could carry. It would last him several days. He would be in the mountains and might not find game enough to keep him from starvation. It would not be pleasant to starve in the mountains . . . He stood up, trembling. His knife dropped from his hands.

No!

He could not do it.

The picture of the old Indian and the little boy, helpless, starving, haunted him. The old father, Tecangretanego. How often had he shared his last bit of hard bread with James—and gladly shared it! How often had he given James his last pinch of tobacco —that most precious of his possessions—bought with many fur pelts from the traders.

No, the old man must not die that death of slow starvation!

James turned back.

The twelve miles back to camp seemed never-ending. The moon was high in the sky when he returned, but he made a fire and cooked some of the meat for the old man and the boy.

"Come!" he called, and the words seemed to be an echo of another voice heard long ago. "Eat hearty—we have plenty of meat now."

Other days of hunger. Tontileaugo! He had spoken those words. Hungry days had gone before, hungry days might come again. Yesterday Tontileaugo gave him meat, today James gave meat to Tecangretanego. Tomorrow the gesture would go on, for the Indians pledged themselves to love and defend one another, and as long as there was a bite of meat and a crumb of cornbread it would be shared with one's brother.

As the winter days passed into early spring the rheumatism left Tecangretanego, and they planned to go by canoe down the Olentangy. They found the river low and, waiting for high water, James found Tecangretanego praying for rain. He began his petition to the Great Being with thanks for the cure of his rheumatism and concluded:

"Grant that rain may come to raise the Olentangy two or three feet that we may go in safety down to Scioto without danger of our canoe being wrecked on the rocks . . . I now make a present of the last tobacco I have as a free burnt offering . . . I expect thou wilt hear and grant these requests and I thy servant will return thee thanks and love thee for thy gifts."

James doubted that the old Indian's prayer would be effective. Nevertheless, when two days later the rains came and the journey was begun, Tecangretanego was certain his prayer had been answered and James respected the old man's faith.

At Sunyendeand they caught rock fish in the creek, fishing at night with torches and striking the fish with spears as they rose to the surface.

On to the north they went, to Detroit, and into Canada to Caughnewaga, an ancient Indian town nine miles above Montreal. Here news came, in July, of a French ship with English prisoners who were to be exchanged.

"If I could be one of those prisoners!" thought James.

The idea obsessed him. Five years of Indian life had changed his appearance, his habits, his whole existence—but it had not changed his longing for home. Here at last was an opportunity to escape.

"I *will* be one of those prisoners," he decided.

He slipped away one night and privately joined the ship. With the other Englishmen he was imprisoned in Montreal while the negotiations for their exchange were under way. Days dragged into weeks, weeks into months.

Five months passed, and at last the English prisoners were sent to Crown Point, where the exchange was made.

Home! James lost no time in going to Pennsylvania. He was with his own people. He was in his own house. He was dressed again as he used to be. He was once again James Smith, Pennsylvanian.

But through the years he seemed to hear the words of Tecangretanego wherever he went, whatever he did:

"You have given evidence of your fortitude, skill, and resolution, and we hope you will always go on to do great actions, as it is only great actions that make a great man."

·[7]·

The Burning of Kittanning

THE INDIANS are constantly attacking our plantations. Send us a guard for protection. Send us soldiers from the fort to protect us while we gather in our grain." The plea came to Fort Granville (now Lewistown) in 1756 from the settlers of the Tuscarora Valley.

"But what about the fort? What about the Indians lurking here? How can we leave the fort unprotected?" asked a young soldier.

"Oh, you know those Delawares! They are always skulking around. They won't attack the fort. They go after the settlers, one plantation at a time, burning the house and carrying off the people they don't murder in cold blood. A pretty business!"

"They attack an unarmed farmer, but they won't attack an armed force at Fort Granville," another soldier added bitterly. "I'd like a chance to tell those Delawares what I think of them—with bullets!"

"A handful of soldiers can guard the fort," reasoned Lieutenant Edward Armstrong. He looked about him at the men, restless and anxious for active duty.

"Sergeant Ward," he directed, "you will march with a detachment of men from the garrison to Tuscarora Valley, there to protect the lives and property of our people. Should you be needed at the fort we will send scouts to you."

The greater number of the defenders of the fort were glad to go on this mission. Only a score of soldiers were left in the fort, and the women and children stayed under their protection.

Peter Walker stood on guard, his keen eyes alert to any travelers along the worn paths. He gripped his gun and held his breath as a figure broke through the underbrush.

"Just the Buchanan boy," he said to himself and breathed again, relaxing his hold on the gun. The Buchanan family lived some distance from Fort Granville.

"Well, son," he called, as young Buchanan came inside the fort, "have you come to help us keep the fort?"

"I've come to tell you we are on our way to Carlisle," said the youngster.

"Carlisle! So Arthur Buchanan is taking his family to a safer part of the country, is he? He doesn't like the Indians?"

"You know the Shawnee chief, Kishacoquillas, is our friend," explained young Buchanan. "He sent us word that the Delawares are getting ready for an attack."

"Reports get worse and worse," commented Peter. "The Delawares are around all the time, but we can't do much about it."

"What makes them hate us so?" asked the boy.

"Well," said Peter slowly, "it's a long story. First they hated the Iroquois. They used to be bitter foes. The Iroquois conquered them and made them act as peacemakers in some of the wars. Peacemaking in Indian tribes is the women's job, so you see, the Delawares were no longer considered as Indian braves, but as women!"

"They would hate that!" nodded the boy.

"Then," continued Peter, "along came the white men, and they bought land from the Iroquois. But the Iroquois sold land that the Delawares claimed belonged rightly to them! The white men are on the land that the Delawares claimed, so that makes them fight against us."

"It's not fair!" said young Buchanan.

"No, it's not fair," agreed Peter, "but the English didn't realize the lands belonged to the Delawares. The English paid for the lands once, so they can't understand why they must pay for them all over again, and so they fight to keep them!"

"Our friend Kishacoquillas tells us that the Delawares have a town of their own back in the woods," the boy waved his hand toward the west, "and they have their own trail over the mountains."

"So that's where they go!" said Peter. "Down the Tuscarora, over the mountains, and all the way to the West!"

"The name of the town is Kittanning. It means Great River. Kishacoquillas told us."

"Well, son, if they'd stay in their town life would be a whole lot pleasanter for all of us!"

"Yes," said the boy, "and then we wouldn't have to move to Carlisle."

"Well, you keep your eyes and ears open. And you tell your father Peter Walker says he has the right idea about Indians—making friends with them."

"Yes," said young Buchanan, "but not all Indians are like Kishacoquillas!"

He walked away, but turned again and made a gesture of farewell. Peter watched him as he disappeared down the path into the underbrush. He was as lithe and agile as an Indian. Life on the frontier made boys like that, alert and wary, and with strength and courage far beyond their years.

From all sides had come reports about the bloody warfare that the Delawares were waging against the settlers. The Indian chief, Captain Jacobs, and his warriors had preyed upon lonely settlers but seemed to have no inclination to attack the numerous forts built in a chain along the western frontier. Terror reigned throughout the settlements. As Peter Walker thought of the many months Captain Jacobs and his Delawares had been at their murderous work his body grew tense, and his fingers gripped his gun. He scowled and his eyes blazed in anger.

Suddenly he crouched forward, staring.

Indians! Speak of them, think of them, and there they were! They seemed to appear as if by magic, rising out of the ground. One here, one there, another, then another.

While he gaped at them the fort was surrounded.

"Indians!" yelled Peter Walker, rallying the soldiers near him. "And French, too!"

From every side the men leaped to their positions. Yes, the French. Without them the Indians would not have dared an attack upon the fort. The French soldiers issued commands; the Indians obeyed them.

Throughout the afternoon and night the Indians fired against the fort without success.

"No damage of any account," reported Peter Walker in the early morning.

"No," agreed Lieutenant Armstrong, "but how much ammunition do they have? We have not much left in the fort, and no way to get more. And I distrust them. They never fight as we expect them to."

As he spoke a thin trail of smoke appeared at the end of the stockade, and one of the men came running.

"Fire!" he cried. "They've come up by the ravine. They're burning out a hole in the logs!"

"We'll be burned alive!" gasped a soldier named John Turner. "Let me talk to them in their own language. I speak French!"

"The first word of French you speak, you die!" thundered Lieutenant Armstrong.

"We'll never yield the fort. Hold out," he shouted to his men. "The flame is falling, and we'll soon put it out."

The soldiers were frantically digging up clay to quench the fire. But through the widening hole came shots, and four soldiers fell, one of them killed outright, the three others wounded. Lieutenant Armstrong himself was a direct target.

"We'll never yield the fort!" repeated the brave lieutenant and fell with a bullet in his heart.

The garrison became panic-stricken.

"Surrender! Surrender!" shouted the French.

The soldiers in the fort held a hurried consultation. What was to be done? Was there any hope of getting reënforcements?

"No scout could get through to Fort Shirley."

"What about ammunition?"

"We can't hold out much longer."

"And water! We've got to have water!"

This was the second day without water.

Could they trust the French? Would their lives be saved if they surrendered? Women and children were there to be considered. They must not be killed or taken captive.

"Don't surrender for our sakes," said the women. "Hold out! There may yet be hope!"

"Listen!" said Peter Walker. "What's that?"

It was the creaking of the great gate.

"It's John Turner! John Turner!" shouted Peter, aghast. "Are you mad?"

Before the men could leap to stop him, John Turner had forcibly swung back the heavy gate, and the Indians were inside. Fort Granville had been betrayed.

Resistance was out of the question.

Captivity or death, that was all that could be expected now.

John Turner stood at the gate. Undoubtedly he expected the Indians to be grateful. But the Indians despised traitors and knew what to do with them. He was the first man to be taken and bound.

The rest of the prisoners—twenty-two men, three women, and a number of children—were loaded down with plunder from the fort and the settlers' houses. They were roped together and driven forth by the savages to begin the long march to Kittanning. Staggering along, they heard the roar of the fire behind them, the snapping and crackling of the logs, as the flames reduced Fort Granville to ashes.

Peter Walker plodded on with the rest of the prisoners, but over and over in his mind he kept repeating, "I must escape. I must escape."

Perhaps in every mind the same thought persisted. The prisoners knew that they could not hope for mercy from their captors, but they took a sort of solace in being huddled together, in sharing a common fate. The days seemed almost endless. Every day seemed like the one before.

At Kittanning many of the prisoners were tortured. Some were killed. Some died lingering and wretched deaths. Some tried to run away. When those who did so were brought back to the town, they were treated more cruelly than before. But Peter Walker still hoped to elude his savage captors.

One day he escaped into the wild forest land, and the prisoners at Kittanning looked at one another with a faint gleam of hope in their eyes.

"Will they find him? Will they bring him back? Or will he get away and bring help to deliver us? Will he go to the governor?"

Day after day passed.

.   .   .

Colonel John Armstrong received Peter Walker at Carlisle. The news of Lieutenant Armstrong's death at Fort Granville had stirred the wrath of the colonel and he determined to avenge his brother's death without delay. Peter Walker's story strengthened his determination.

"The whole western frontier is exposed to these attacks by the Indians," said Peter. "Everywhere there is confusion and terror."

"Reports come to me of the most hideous atrocities," agreed the colonel.

"Much worse than death," continued Peter, "is the agony of a prisoner's life. The fiendish cruelties the Indians can devise! I can never forget what I have seen and what I have experienced." He described in detail the death of Turner, the traitor.

"The rest of the captives must be rescued!" declared Peter. "It is slow torment. Even now, who knows their fate? And the frontier settlers are constantly being captured and taken to Kittanning. Even the forts are not safe. Captain Jacobs has said that he can take any fort that will catch fire!"

"We'll wipe out Kittanning!" swore Colonel Armstrong. "And I shall take particular pains to wipe out Captain Jacobs. I have written to the governor and to Benjamin Franklin. And now, at last, the governor has permitted me to arrange my expedition. I have three hundred men, and we'll wipe Kittanning off the face of the earth!"

Out of Fort Shirley Colonel Armstrong marched his three hundred militiamen. He was determined to reach Kittanning before another raid through the valley brought new horror. In three days he reached a place near what is now Hollidaysburg, where he took to the Kittanning Trail. After following it for two days through the woods, he arrived at a point fifty miles from the Indian village, and there he camped.

He called Peter Walker and another scout.

"You will go ahead to Kittanning," he ordered, "and bring back a report of the number of Indians, the disposition of the village, and the vantage points from which an attack can be made."

The two men took provisions of bread, venison, powder, and shot, looked to their knives, and set out at once.

Two days passed.

Colonel Armstrong waited. On the second day Peter and the other scout returned.

"The trail is clear," they reported. "Kittanning is quiet. The Indians seem occupied with their own affairs, and no preparations for expeditions of any sort are evident."

"Nevertheless," warned the colonel, "we must proceed with caution."

He ordered the men forward. The scouts were sent ahead to report any new alarms or perils.

All went well until they were about six miles from Kittanning, when Peter reported a band of red men around a fire by the trail.

Colonel Armstrong stood thinking.

"We won't attack them," he decided at last. "We're too near the town; an attack would disclose our presence. We'll leave some men with Lieutenant Hogg to keep them covered until morning."

The column moved forward.

The trees threw long interlocking shadows, and strips of light fell across the narrow trail, for the moon was full and high. The men were silent. Mile after mile, day after day, their feet had sunk into the soft forest mold of leaves and earth. Now they circled the hills surrounding Kittanning. As they emerged from the woods into the full light of the moon, they saw below them the Allegheny River, twisting and glistening in the soft light, and beside it in the valley lay the log huts, separated from the hill by cornfields. From the Indian village came the sound of beating tom-toms and chanting.

As Colonel Armstrong stood counting the huts below to esti-mate the number of inhabitants, he was startled by a strange whistle that came from the cornfield between his position on the hill and the edge of the Indian village.

"Are we discovered?" he asked, turning to his guide. Peter Walker knew every custom and sign of these Indians.

"No, sir," he said. "That is an Indian brave leaving the dance. He will make a fire now, shoot off his gun, clean it, and lie down to sleep."

"He won't sleep long," the colonel promised himself.

"Be ready to attack," he directed.

In the moonlight he disposed his troops. The main body stayed

The fire burned furiously, sending the Indians scurrying from their huts.

above the cornfield overlooking the lower part of the town. A number of officers directed their men along the east side of the town, taking the utmost care to move the lines quietly around the village in order to surround it before the order came to attack.

Below the hill, in the cornfield, a small fire flared up.

"What's that, Peter? Is it a signal?" asked Colonel Armstrong. "Look! There's another—and another!"

Peter laughed.

"Those fires, sir," he answered, "are only to keep off the gnats. The warriors are going to sleep after their dance."

The night began to lighten into the first gray of morning. Now was the time to strike!

"Ready!" came the command. "Let's go!"

Down through the cornfield swept the colonel's men.

Up jumped the Indian warriors. Roused from sleep, they yelled and ran pellmell to the village. A war whoop roused the people in the huts. The whole village was instantly in turmoil. Squaws and children sped from their homes toward the lower woods. The white forces moved in.

Shots rang from the village and from the cornfield. From the house of Captain Jacobs came a rapid fire, and Colonel Armstrong, drawing near, saw that it was like a small blockhouse, with a loft and loopholes. Most of the braves were stationed there, and the invaders' bullets had little effect.

"They're well protected, and they may have a good supply of powder," thought the colonel, as he directed his men from a doorway near the house. He felt a sudden sharp pain in his shoulder and reeled against the wall. As he staggered from the doorway his arm hung useless.

"Fire the houses!" he commanded.

"Fire the houses!" The cry was repeated.

Torches blazed. Thin curls of smoke drifted upwards from the log walls.

"Surrender! Surrender!" the soldiers cried.

"We are men! We will die fighting!" retorted the Indians.

"You will burn!" shouted the militiamen.

"But we will kill you first!" responded the Indians.

Tongues of flame licked the dried logs of the wall. Smoke swirled upwards. In some places the fire burned furiously, scorching the faces of the soldiers, sending the Indians scurrying from hidden corners of their huts. The hottest flames encircled Captain Jacob's house. A keg of powder blew up with a deafening roar.

The heat increased. It became more and more intense and suffocating, until the attackers were forced to withdraw to a point beyond the fire. With the white prisoners they had rescued, they took up a position where they could fire at the Indians who tried to escape into the cornfield.

Explosions shook the earth around them. The air was filled with splinters of wood that burst into flame and fell, to burn furiously in the wreckage. The noise of the blasts rent the air for miles.

At the cockloft door of Captain Jacob's house appeared the head and shoulders of an Indian. Quickly aimed, a bullet tumbled him forward out of the loft. Was it Captain Jacobs? No one could be sure. It was almost impossible to get to the body because of the fire. Finally it was reached. The powder horn and the bullet pouch were French, but the scalp lock was thought to be that of Captain Jacobs. Colonel Armstrong took a grim satisfac-

tion in these articles. He had avenged the death of his brother
Edward. What did it matter if his arm hung limp? He smiled
wryly as the blood soaked his shoulder and breast, and one of
his aides tried to staunch the flow and bind the wound.

Peter Walker reported to him.

"It might be well to begin the return," he said. "I saw a band
of these Indians down the river. They may have been on their
way for help. They might cut off our return."

"We will not leave until every house has been fired," the
colonel stated in determined tones. "We are here to destroy Kittanning to the last log, and destroy it we will."

"This very day," one of the rescued prisoners told Armstrong,
"two bateaux of Delawares and French soldiers were expected to
join Captain Jacobs in the village. Tomorrow morning they were
all to have set out to take Fort Shirley."

"They called that Croghan's Fort," added another. "The Indians thought they had enough powder to fight against the
English for ten years."

"Every house was stored with it," said still another prisoner.
"But it certainly is going up in smoke—and going up fast."

"As for that band of Indians down the river," said one of the
youngest prisoners, "last night they sent out twenty-four warriors; whether they were an advance party planning to attack
the settlements or headed for Fort Shirley, or whether they went
for food, of course we can't know."

"Ah," said Colonel Armstrong to Peter, "that accounts for the
Indians you saw. And probably some of them were the Indians
Lieutenant Hogg was left to attack at daybreak."

A terrific explosion rocked the ground under their feet. (Later
it was learned that the blast was heard as far away as Fort

Duquesne!) In a great cone of fire, the top of Captain Jacob's house was blown into the air and with it the bodies of some of the warriors who had taken refuge there. The village was now one great sheet of flame. The blaze enveloped every house, sweeping through and leaving only charred ruins and smoking embers. As they sank in flames, the warriors could be heard singing the death chant.

Kittanning was no longer a stronghold of hostile Indians.

Kittanning was reduced to charred and smoking ruins.

Never again would the Indians feel safe and secure in their strongholds. At last fear had entered their hearts.

·[8]·

How Pittsburgh Got Its Name

A T FORT DUQUESNE the French flag flew in victorious possession. Nine years had passed since Trader Croghan sent
to the governor of Pennsylvania the French scalp that
the Indians had given him in token of their allegiance, and it
had been four years since Washington had surrendered Fort
Necessity. In those four years many scalps had been taken, both
French and British. Four years of hostilities, four years of fighting for the control of the fur trade and the wealth of the western
borderlands. The British still asserted their rights, still con-
tested the French possession of the Ohio Valley.

In the spring of 1758 the British armies once more prepared
to march against Fort Duquesne at the forks of the Ohio.

They were more than three hundred miles away.

General Forbes sat in his white-paneled quarters in New York.
A young aide stood beside him, waiting for the letter the general
was writing to Governor Denny of Pennsylvania:

" . . . and therefore must beg that the Officers and Soldiers raised
in Pennsylvania for the Service are Able Bodied good Men,
capable of enduring fatigue, and that their arms be the best that
can be found in the Province; as Carpenters and Axe Men are
absolutely necessary upon Many Occasions, I must recommend

103

the sending as many of those as can be conveniently got into the troops . . ."

The general's quill scratched on down the paper.

"I am informed that the Inhabitants upon the Frontiers of your Province, being much used to hunting in the Woods, would consequently make good Rangers, In which case I am to beg you will give your direction for the forming some of your properest Men into Companys of Rangers with good Officers, who are well acquainted with the country, to command them."

The general moved in his chair, crossed one silk-stockinged leg over the other, then folded the paper, addressed it, and sealed it with red wax into which he pressed his gold-mounted signet. He handed the letter to the aide.

"You will carry this to Governor Denny, and hand him also this packet, to be sent by express to Virginia. You will await His Excellency's reply and bring it to me at once."

The young man saluted, swung on his heel, and strode from the room.

General Forbes pushed aside the papers and the quill and leaned his forehead against his arm. The officers standing by the fireplace looked at one another and shook their heads soberly.

A scabbard clattered against a chair as a young captain stepped forward.

"Had you not best retire, sir? You do yourself harm to abuse your strength so."

The general raised his head. His face was as white as the ruffles of his shirt.

"You will have the goodness to attend to your own business," he growled.

"I regret, sir," said the captain, but he kept his stand and met the general's frown with a look of quiet determination. The general looked away.

"I too, sir," he said in frank apology for his gruffness. "Give me your arm."

In the inner room the general sank down upon a couch and clenched his teeth in pain.

"There is not a moment he is not in pain," whispered an officer in the outer room. "He is really ill. But he has an iron will and goes on in spite of everything. No wonder he is called the Head of Iron."   •   •   •

There were so many details, so many things to be arranged! Another letter to the governor:

"Sir: As there will be a Number of Waggons and Carriages wanted in the Province of Pennsylvania, and as the Inhabitants may be backward in furnishing of them, altho' to be payed for them with ready Money, I therefore take this opportunity of letting you know that Warrants to impress the Waggons will be necessary all over the Province. If you are not vested with the Power to grant such Warrants, will you apply to the Assembly to grant them, and fix prices upon the Different Carriages and Horses. I have the Honour to be, Sir, Your most Obedient and most humble Servant, Jo. Forbes."

In April the general established headquarters in Philadelphia, and April passed into May, and May into June, while he waited there for troops and supplies from England, and waited also for news from the province of Maryland, which was proving dilatory in raising the quota of militia for the expedition. The Cherokee and Catawba Indians had gathered as they had promised: six hundred and fifty of them, at Winchester, Virginia, were actually ready to join the forces in the West that General Forbes had already sent there. Regular troops were marching from South Carolina.

Scouting parties, equipped for war, reconnoitered above and below Fort Duquesne, annoying the enemy, gathering intelligence, trying to take prisoners for information.

No news had come from Fort Duquesne since June of the year before, when Lieutenant Baker had reported six hundred French soldiers and two hundred Indians there. Other reports placed the strength of the garrison at anywhere from two hundred to six hundred. It was said that the Delawares were moving up the Allegheny and that they could be persuaded to ally themselves with the English.

General Forbes waited impatiently for news from his advance scouts. He waited impatiently for the supplies which had been promised by William Pitt, prime minister of England, who had made this expedition possible.

It was while the general and his staff were at dinner one evening in June that the transports were sighted sailing up the river and the near-by guns boomed a salute.

General Forbes rose from the table.

"Gentlemen, there are the store ships, with arms, tents, ammunition, and artillery. We can soon set out directly for the frontier. You will have the goodness, gentlemen, to keep your places and make an end of your dinner. It will be some time before they make fast their moorings. I shall, however, oversee the landing."

But the general did not oversee the landing. He could not walk across the room. He stood, crouching with pain, his face drawn, his whole body taut with agony. His teeth bit into his lower lip until a red line of blood trickled down his chin.

Three hundred miles to the fort he was determined to take. Three hundred miles of rough roads, over mountains, through wilderness, with the terrible heat of the summer to endure, and the agonizing pain! He was determined to do it. His courage was indomitable.

On the last day of June the troops left Philadelphia. Artillery wagons rattled over the cobblestones, the iron-shod hoofs of the horses clattered and rang through the din, the children shouted along the streets and laughed with delight as Montgomery's Highland battalion passed with its bagpipes playing and kilts of the marching men swaying in rhythm, line after line. The British soldiers, in their gay scarlet coats and buff breeches swung along to the music of fife and drum.

"Victory! Victory!" shouted the bystanders, waving their hats and their handkerchiefs, cheering the marching soldiers as they turned out of the town along the broad highway.

West! The road stretched endlessly ahead. Three hundred miles to the high bluff above the three great rivers.

The summer heat became excessive. There was no shade as the hot sun rose each day in a cloudless sky. The Susquehanna River had to be crossed on rafts and flats that tilted and rocked dangerously.

At Carlisle—the frontier town, now that the Indian raids had frightened the settlers from the country farther west—the streets were crowded with troops, with pack-horse trains arriving and departing, with Indians, with horses and cattle and wagon trains.

At Shippensburg General Forbes dismounted at the tavern, climbed the worn stairway up to his rooms, and wearily directed his young aide to write a letter at his dictation.

"To His Excellency, the Governor of Pennsylvania," he began.

"Dear Sir: I cannot paint the misery and distress that I have been in since I had the pleasure of seeing you. . . . I now begin to mend a little, and hope in a day or two to gitt forward, where tho' my presence be necessary, yet my absence creates no stop in carrying on our publick affairs. Our new road advances apace, so that in a few days I hope to have our advance post on the other side of Laurel Hill pretty well towards the Enemy.

"My pain obliges me to make use of another Hand writing than my own which I know you have goodness enough to excuse."

The general's dictation was interrupted by a knock at the door. A scouting party had returned from the Ohio with two scalps taken within half a mile of Fort Duquesne.

"And what intelligence have you?" asked the general, forcing his words as the old pain stabbed through him.

"Sir, little that is not known," said the scout. "It seems there are about fifty Indian huts near the fort, and a garrison, we believe, sir, of from three to four hundred white men."

"Good enough," said the general, "but you will return and again attempt to make your way as close as possible to the fort. Try to find Mr. Andrew Montour. Proceed under his instructions, for he knows the fort. You must determine the number of French Canadians there. You must find out if there are intrenchments before the fort, between the Monongahela and the Allegheny; what has been built lately either at the fort or at the other side of the river; what guns are mounted; what men leave the fort during the day and night to reconnoiter."

"Yes, sir," said the scout, keenly attentive.

"You will then report to the post nine miles beyond Loyalhanna, on the other side of the Chestnut Ridge. You will make yourselves known by wearing yellow bands about your heads and arms, and by waving your matchcoats on long poles."

The general turned his face to the wall. He closed his eyes, to bear the pain that gripped him. His hand fell heavily at his side.

The captain opened his portfolio and waited for the letter to be finished, but the general made no move. The captain sat by his side, silent. In a few minutes, by the regular breathing, he knew that the general, exhausted by fatigue and suffering, had dropped into a deep sleep.

.   .   .

General Forbes studied the map spread before him and traced a finger along a new route over the mountains.

"Colonel Bouquet has carefully studied the reports of the scouts," he said to his staff, as they gathered about him at the table. "He points out that this new road will afford direct communication with the farms of the East, so that food and other supplies for the army may be easily obtained. Part of its course follows the old road that Colonel Burd started three years ago."

"Such a road would afford easy access to the Ohio Valley," remarked one of the men.

"That would not please the Virginians," replied another. "They want the Ohio Valley for themselves, not for Pennsylvanians."

"Colonel Washington is, of course, in favor of the old Braddock road," declared General Forbes. "It is true that it is nineteen miles shorter. But the old road is grown up with brush and timber. Either road we decide upon will have to be constructed. And to save time," said the general, "we can station cutters and axmen at various points to work both ways at once."

The recommendation from Colonel Bouquet was accepted, and orders were issued for cutting through the new road. Colonel

Washington and his Virginians chafed and complained, and no doubt Colonel Bouquet faltered in his determination when he found what a prodigious amount of work the new road entailed. Cutting, hewing, blasting their way through the mountainous wilderness, enlarging and strengthening stockades at the old forts, constructing intrenchments and palisades, erecting new fortifi- cations—the troops accomplished their great tasks in less than three months.

General Forbes was carried in a litter between two horses, his suffering was so exhausting.

"Captain," he said to his young aide, "it may be that I shall not see the taking of Fort Duquesne. My health, precarious for the past two years, has of late been a great weariness to me. This long period of pain has drained my very life out of me. I should die happy, however, could I dispatch news to London that I had accomplished what no one else has been able to do—take and hold the forks of the Ohio for Britain. I should like to be the one to bring success to His Majesty's arms in this expedition. I cannot think we shall fail this time!"

The captain listened compassionately.

"I am sure you will do it, sir," he said.

"You will forgive my talk of my own difficulties," said the general. "I am worn out and not myself. There are difficulties everywhere, and yet I have done everything in my power to carry forward this expedition. I believe we have planned well."

"Surely no one could have given more thought or more personal effort," said the aide. "Do me the honor, sir, to attend you here while you rest, as you should, for several days. The troops can move forward to Raystown or Loyalhanna, and there you can direct their final movements."

The general was silent.

"Captain," he said at last, "I shall move with the men tomorrow. I shall leave nothing undone on my part that can in the smallest way contribute to the success of our cause. I do well enough in my litter."

Hour after hour the litter swung between the horses plodding up the long hills. The general's face was sunken and gray. The hollows of his cheeks deepened, the nose sharpened; the eyes, heavy with pain, were lifeless. At times, however, they revealed a desperate will to live, to act, to accomplish this last service for his country.

At Raystown (Bedford) all the forces of the expedition gathered together: southern militia from Maryland and Virginia, rangers from Pennsylvania, Indian allies from Winchester, and British troops. Colonel Bouquet with his British regulars was at Loyalhanna (Ligonier).

"We have progressed to the very beard of the enemy!" they exulted.

The whole army of six thousand men was ready to attack that enemy, and with good fortune the attack should not fail.

·   ·   ·

Major James Grant sat with Colonel Bouquet at the camp at Loyalhanna.

"Give me five hundred men," begged the major. "We will reconnoiter the fort."

"Such a move, major, would disclose our presence before it is time to attack. My plan is to send two companies of a hundred men each, and they can occupy the paths and cut off the enemy in their ambush."

"The garrison is not over six hundred, French soldiers and Indians," persisted Major Grant. "By erecting an ambuscade we can take many prisoners and not be discovered, and beside we can keep a constant watch over the roads and the enemy."

Colonel Bouquet was reluctant to give his consent to this scheme. He sent for Colonel Burd and Major Lewis and laid the plan before them. After much discussion Major Grant's plan was agreed to, but he was instructed not to advance close to the fort and not to attack it. The fate of General Braddock's army was still fresh in their memories and they wanted no repetition of that disaster.

But Major Grant was filled with the regular soldier's contempt for cautious colonials. With seven hundred men he marched to the hill overlooking Fort Duquesne and now known by his name. He sent out some officers and Indians to reconnoiter, with orders to kill or capture any French soldiers or Indians outside the fort. The scouts returned, undiscovered, with no report. The temptation to attack the fort then proved too great for the major to withstand. What glory, to capture this fort himself!

Early in the morning he ordered an attack.

The garrison in the fort awoke to the shrill music of bagpipes and the beating of drums.

It was Captain MacDonald's company of Highlanders advancing on the fort at Major Grant's order.

The playing of the bagpipes gave the French and Indians ample time to separate their forces into three divisions and surround the British. As a result Major Grant's forces were shamefully overwhelmed and defeated. Panic followed. Some of the soldiers tried to escape to the river. Many drowned. Hundreds were killed and wounded.

Major Grant and Major Lewis were captured, together with nineteen other officers. On the hill above the French fort seven officers and two hundred and seventy British soldiers lay dead.

.   .   .

The commandant of Fort Duquesne lost no time in following up his victory over Grant, and a large force of French soldiers and Indians marched to Loyalhanna to attack the British fort. There, although they fought with great fury, the British fire forced them to retreat.

After that defeat the French began to be disheartened. The Indian allies dispersed to their homes for the winter; the Louisiana and Illinois militia left the fort; the supplies being sent from Fort Frontenac were destroyed by the enemy.

General Forbes was about to go into winter quarters at Loyalhanna. The roads were impassable. The early snow and sleet spread discomfort through the camp. A thousand details had to be attended to without delay: blankets, winter clothes, flannel jackets, stockings and shoes for all the men . . .

"An English prisoner, sir, from Fort Duquesne," an orderly announced from the door. "Captured with an Indian and squaw."

"Bring me the Englishman," directed General Forbes.

"You may attack the fort with confidence," said the Englishman. "The attempt that was made at Loyalhanna was to make you believe that the French numbers were great. As a matter of fact, the garrison is small. The Indians have gone for the winter. They fear the Long Knives—the Virginians. But the last news, and most depressing it was, concerned the destruction of the supplies they expected for the winter. That has caused them much worry."

At last the time had come to act. In the morning General Forbes ordered the advance of his troops.

Without wagons or baggage, the troops moved forward. The ground was firm and frozen. For four days the columns pressed on, moving slowly, steadily over the last mountain, over the last foothills, until the level route near the rivers made the marching easier. The entire army was within twelve miles of the fort.

"We shall sleep in the fort before another night passes," exclaimed the general.

His confidence again put new strength into his exhausted men.

At midnight the whole camp was startled by a dull, heavy explosion.

"What was that?" the soldiers asked one another.

"The fort! The magazine at the fort has blown up!"

General Forbes stood with uplifted head.

A great exaltation shook his emaciated form. The fort itself was nothing. Let it burn! He could now possess this land for Great Britain. His eyes flashed with new life.

The army advanced early in the morning. Where Fort Duquesne had been they found a heap of smoldering ruins, charred and smoking chimney stacks, and blackened walls. Shouts of joy filled the air as the general was helped from his litter and stood on the ground, which he claimed for Great Britain.

"For king and country!"

The British flag was raised over the smoldering ruins. A shout of triumph echoed and reëchoed from the hills. The long months of toil and hardship were justified. French dominion in that place was at an end.

"This place shall be named Pittsbourgh," announced General Forbes, "in honor of William Pitt, prime minister of England."

Shouts rang through the valley.

"Pittsbourgh!"

"Pittsbourgh!"

And thus on November 25, 1758 did the future iron and steel capital of the world appropriately receive its name from the Head of Iron.

·[9]·

Fort Pitt Holds Out

SPRING thaws and heavy rains flooded the Allegheny and
Monongahela rivers in March of 1763. The two swollen
streams joined at the Point to make a churning whirlpool
below Fort Pitt, and the water surged up and over the banks,
spreading through the broad triangle of land, pounding against
the sides of the fort until the ramparts collapsed into the moat.

On the third day the rivers fell.

Captain Ecuyer walked out to look at the mud and the rubble
of dead wood left in the wake of the receding waters; then he
lost no time in ordering the garrison to make a thorough cleans-
ing of the fort, inside and out. The doors and windows were flung
open, the floors were scraped and washed and allowed to dry in
the wind. The ramparts were quickly repaired and the mud was
shoveled from the moat.

The flood covered the grain fields with a thick deposit of mud,
which dried and cracked in the wind and sun and made the clear-
ings look barren and desolate until after the spring planting.
While guards from the fort kept watch for marauding Indians, the
settlers hurriedly plowed and sowed their fields. Prowling bands
of Indians in the vicinity of Fort Pitt scalped stragglers in the
woods, drove off straying cattle, lurked behind cabins and houses

116

to kill or capture unwary settlers, burned barns and stables, destroyed the growing grain.

The whole frontier was panic-stricken, and rumors flew thick and fast. Messengers from other forts brought the same reports.

"Indians! Indians!"

The cry was heard all through the western valleys.

"It's a general Indian uprising," thought Captain Ecuyer as he listened to the stories of the hunters and traders who came to Fort Pitt. "All the western tribes seem to be banded together. And Pontiac is the leader. Well, if we are not able to escape their tomahawks, at least we can be prepared for their attack."

"There is a plan to attack all the forts at once," reported one of the scouts.

"They'll not take Fort Pitt," declared the captain. "We have men, provisions, and ammunition to defend it, and defend it we will."

He began to make preparations. Every soldier, hunter, and trader stood ready to defend the fort from sudden assault. The whole garrison was armed, and every man was ordered to have his gun by him at all hours of the day and night. The settlers fled from their homes and, bringing their few possessions, crowded inside the protecting walls of the fort, abject and miserable. Their cabins and houses were torn down and cleared away.

"The Indians will have no chance to hide in those houses," said Captain Ecuyer grimly. "They won't be able to get very close to the fort without protection, so we'll clear the land as much as we can."

To Colonel Bouquet he wrote:

"We are so crowded in the fort that I fear disease: in spite of every care, I cannot keep the place as clean as I should like. Besides, the smallpox is among us; and I have therefore caused a hospital to be built under the drawbridge, out of range of musket shot."

The scouts, trying to communicate with the outside world, were forced to turn back. The Indians harried the English with bold persistence, even announcing their presence at the very walls of the fort by firing at the sentinels from time to time. The sporadic raids had finally culminated in a siege. With all his thoughts centered on safety and protection, the captain remembered the smaller outposts and tried to send messages of warning. Again he wrote to Colonel Bouquet, "I am Uneasy for the little Posts—as for this, I will answer for it."

It was this confidence in himself and his men that inspired the refugees who had fled to Fort Pitt for protection. Captain Ecuyer and his Royal Americans could save them all. They put themselves unreservedly into the captain's hands, and he ordered their daily routine as he ordered that of his soldiers. Through the days and weeks he personally supervised the smallest details, issuing a hundred rules and regulations:

"See that no one leaves the fort without permission or without a heavy guard. All log cutting, field work, or necessary outside business must be done under guard.

"Mount the artillery, and see that the platforms are solid and stable.

"Let the traders set their beaver traps outside the palisades. Our prowling night-visitors may learn to keep their distance! The crowfeet traps, also. They are pointed enough to bite through deerskin moccasins.

"Sleep on your guns, men. Everyone must be double armed.

"Let the women, in case of attack, serve water to the men on

"Now then, Paddy," he said, and the figure was hoisted above the stockade. A bullet struck the dummy at once.

duty. And above all, make no sound in going backwards and forwards in the fort, I warn you!

"All dogs and horses must be tied up. Cattle will be watered once a day and fed with spelt twice daily."

The men and women, under a guard of thirty soldiers, cut the wheat-like spelt in the nearest fields with sickles, spread it out to dry in the sun, and stacked it to be ready for the cattle when needed. The spelt in the other fields remained uncut. There was much work to be done, both in the fort and out, and anyone refusing to do his share was confined to the guardhouse. There was no room for lazy men or selfish women. The orders continued:

"To save water, the women shall do the washings at the boat house in the lower town, twice a week only, and under guard of a corporal and six privates.

"All chimneys must be swept so the danger of fire may be lessened."

The men were divided into two divisions of sixty-eight or seventy privates, three officers, five sergeants, and one drum. When their arms were ordered unloaded, wiped clean, and loaded again, only half the men were allowed to unload their guns at one time.

As the days passed, danger increased. The people in the fort grew more and more apprehensive. The long summer days intensified discomforts. The fort was hot. The close confinement showed in tired faces and frayed nerves. The days of strain and anxiety had lengthened into weeks and months.

Captain Ecuyer's watchfulness never ceased.

On an afternoon in late June a bold party of Delawares seized the horses and cattle grazing in the field outside the fort and opened fire on the garrison, killing two men. An instant discharge of howitzers was the response from the fort. The bursting shells scattered far and wide and sent the Indians flying in disorder.

In the morning an Indian, Turtle's Heart, surrounded by his tribesmen approached the fort. They had stuck leafy branches in the muzzles of their guns.

"We come out of regard to you, my brothers," said Turtle's Heart to the defenders of the fort. "We want you to leave this place. You promised to go east as soon as you drove the French away, and yet you stay here and build houses, and more and more people come. If, therefore, you will stay, you must know that six nations have taken up the hatchet against you. Pontiac himself has sent us the black wampum and the red-dipped tomahawk."

Captain Ecuyer faced the savage chiefs boldly.

"I will hold the fort against all the Indians in the woods," he cried. "If they come around the fort again, I will blow them to pieces with shells!"

"Brothers, your people will be spared if you go now to the English settlements. If you stay, you will be destroyed by our six nations of the West."

"On the contrary," said Captain Ecuyer, "you yourselves had better hide. I will tell you in confidence that a great army is on its way to Fort Pitt, another great army has gone up the lakes to meet Pontiac, and still another great army has gone to the Virginia frontier where the Cherokee and Catawba will join it. These Indians are your dreaded enemies. They expect to destroy you. No brothers, we are well off here, and will stay. But you had better hide!"

The chiefs looked at each other in great chagrin.

Three armies! These white men were mighty and powerful. The great chiefs withdrew to their painted warriors and, without more ado, dispersed and disappeared into the woods where they could hold a consultation with the tribes.

Captain Ecuyer renewed his watch. He expected an attack daily. He reissued orders for the protection of his people and waited.

Late one night, as the sentinel called out the hour, "Eleven o'clock and all's well," from the Indians on the opposite shore of the Monongahela came the mocking echo:

"All's well!"

"Who'd suspect those grim warriors of prankish humor?" marveled Captain Ecuyer, thinking of the solemn delegation of Indians, headed by Shingiss and Turtle's Heart, that had demanded a second conference at the fort.

"We have a message from Pontiac that he is coming with a great army," they had said. "He and his army are hungry, and they will eat everything in their way."

Shingiss had addressed the captain:

"We wish to hold fast the chain of friendship . . . but you have let your end of the chain fall to the ground. My brothers, this land is ours, not yours. We wish you to go away."

"We shall never abandon this fort as long as a white man lives in America!" Captain Ecuyer had answered.

The chiefs departed in anger and bitter hatred.

Soon after, the Indians began a general attack against the fort. Under cover of darkness they completely surrounded it, and along the banks of the rivers they dug holes where they concealed themselves safely and from which they kept up a steady shower of bullets and arrows. A general fire was opened from

every side. Day after day the attack continued without inter-
mission.

"Let no one fire until he has marked his man," ordered Captain
Ecuyer.

One of the marksmen, known as Brown Bill, had his own ideas
about marking his man. He gathered up some old clothes and
stuffed them with straw.

"Now then, Paddy," he said, and the figure was slowly hoisted
above the stockade by one of Brown Bill's comrades. A bullet
struck the dummy at once, but almost at the same instant, in the
half darkness, Brown Bill sighted the flash from the Indian's gun
and fired.

"Up again, Paddy!" cried Brown Bill.

But his Paddy made too much fun in the fort, and Brown Bill
was disgusted.

"Quiet!" he said to the laughing soldiers. "Now the Indians
suspect a joke, hearing the laughs. Paddy will be no good."

The Indians along the banks caused the most annoyance, and
finally, by the use of a flatboat with high gunwales, the soldiers
anchored in the river and fired upon the dugouts. This was too
much for the Indians. They were between two fires, and it did
not take long to rout them out of their holes and send them
up the Allegheny.

But the siege continued.

The fort was entirely cut off from the outside world. The
summer heat was intense. Flies and mosquitoes bred in the refuse.
The sun dried up the water in the barrels on the ramparts. Firewood became scarce. Washing and ironing were curtailed, to
save water and wood. Food consisted of salt pork and cornmeal.
The King's Gardens, beyond the palisades by the river, could

not be reached. The remaining spelt in the fields needed to be cut if it was not to be lost, but the men did not dare to venture out.

Occasionally the cows could be sent into the nearest meadows, but after three men lost their lives driving the cows from pasture the practice was abandoned.

"But that spelt," thought Captain Ecuyer. Surely a well organized company could harvest the spelt. He called for volunteers. The sickles were sharpened. With bread and cold meat, provisions for the day, the company of volunteers marched out and cut and tied the grain.

In spite of Captain Ecuyer's boast of the supplies and ammunition that were stored in the fort, he knew only too well that he faced an actual dearth of food, of powder and bullets, of firewood, of fodder for the cattle. From the very beginning of the siege he had ordered half rations of bread and meat for the people, and now, on the twenty-eighth of July, as the captain looked over his stores, he was faced with the grim specter of starvation.

"Two weeks, with the most careful planning, the strictest care," he thought. "And then what will happen? If Colonel Bouquet comes to our relief all well and good. But what if he fails us? If we capitulate, the entire garrison will be murdered. If we attempt to cut our way through the enemy, that will be certain suicide. If we take no action at all, we face starvation here." He sighed heavily. "The months are eternal!"

Suddenly, without warning, came the climactic Indian attack.

The desperate and frenzied violence of the onslaught roused the men in the fort to a vigorous and determined response. It was as if during all these long months the energy of the Indians had been stored until it loosed itself at last in a blast of fiendish fury. For five days and nights the fort suffered under constant, deadly fire. The powder dwindled. The stores diminshed. The men at their posts were hollow-cheeked, their eyes sunken and burning with sleeplessness. Twenty of the Indians were killed and wounded. Of the garrison, seven were wounded, Captain Ecuyer among them.

The fifth day dawned, and the assault raged on. But when the sun was at its height Captain Ecuyer thought the firing lessened, and as the afternoon wore on the thought became a certainty.

"The Indians are withdrawing," the soldiers whispered to one another exultantly.

"Look," they cried guardedly. "Look out there—in the river."

The Indians were crossing the Allegheny with their baggage!

The strain of the last five days began to break. Firing against the fort ceased. There were fewer and fewer alarms, and gradually the terror of assault waned. Although the garrison remained vigilant and ready for any surprise, scarcely any Indians were to be seen. All through the first week of August not a feather showed, not an arrow was shot, not a rifle cracked from the woods or the brush outside the fort.

An express managed to get through.

"Colonel Bouquet is at Bedford," reported the man; "he is on his way to Fort Pitt."

Colonel Bouquet at last! Now there was nothing to fear, for Fort Pitt was in touch with the outer world again. Colonel Bouquet would bring supplies. There was an excited hubbub of talk and chatter. The fort became lively and cheerful. Children ran about unrestrained. The men took out their pipes, so long denied them.

But Captain Ecuyer became thoughtful. Why had the Indians

suddenly deserted the fort? Had they known of Colonel Bouquet's march to the relief of the western forts? Had they gone to meet Bouquet's army? Would they fall upon the army in a surprise attack?

The captain felt a cold chill strike at his heart. What was to be done?

He could send reënforcements to Bouquet—but what if the Indians had retired from the siege of the fort only to lie in wait for the soldiers outside? No, the only thing left for him to do was to hold fast and wait.

An express from Colonel Bouquet brought news:

"At Bushy Run the Indians fell upon the army," related the man in great excitement. "Our bayonets broke their charge, but they returned again and again. By pretending to drop back into a retreat we managed to surround them. Then our bayonets routed them. They cannot, will not fight against bayonets. They ran in great confusion, in headlong flight to the woods."

The people of the fort gathered around in great wonderment.

"What does it mean?" asked the children.

"It means the siege is over," shouted the men. "The siege is over and Fort Pitt holds out!"

· [10] ·

When a Fist Was Law

A HORSEMAN appeared over the brow of the hill, rode down into the glade at a gallop, jumped the fallen log across the narrow path, and slowed to a walk so that his horse could safely ford Ten Mile Creek. As he reached the farther bank, Jed Lewis glanced behind him, then raced on, along the horse path, digging his moccasined feet into his horse's ribs. He smiled with satisfaction.

Following behind, Gil Simon on his bay stallion cleared the log easily, splashed through the creek, and galloped up the same path. The bay was powerful, and in spite of the felled trees, the brush, and the ditches he was gaining on the horse ahead.

"Good work, Iroquois," Gil said, smacking his hand against the horse's sleek neck.

There was only a mile to go, and after the turn in the path the way was straight and clear. Without warning, however, the bay stumbled. Gil was thrown suddenly into the brush. The horse snorted and pranced as his rider scrambled out of the underbrush. Gil rode on, but now he was hopelessly behind.

Far ahead, Jed galloped into a clearing and pulled his horse to a sudden halt before a cabin door. He leaped to the ground and turned to wave his cap before he went inside.

Gil spurred his horse and reached the clearing.

"So you beat me, Jed Lewis," he called.

"So I did," answered Jed, coming out of the cabin. He held up a bottle of whiskey. "And here's my prize: good old Black Betty!"

He tucked the bottle under his arm, laughing.

"I'll have to admit, your mare can run," said Gil.

"Sure she can run," replied Jed proudly.

"All the same, I wouldn't trade Iroquois for her, even if he did throw me," and Gil stroked his horse's neck. "Well Jed, it was a lot of fun, riding for the bottle." Now Jed would be privileged to be "best man," to stand with the groom, George Teagarden, at the wedding. But first all the guests must have a drink from Black Betty.

"I'll race you back, Gil," he said. "They'll give us up for lost."

The two riders galloped off gaily.

The wedding procession filed through the woods from the groom's house to that of the bride. George Teagarden led the company, self-conscious and smiling. Following him were the minister and his wife and the older guests. The younger people of the neighborhood straggled along in the best of spirits, laughing, shouting, and playing pranks. Everyone loved a wedding.

Now through the woods and over the obstacles set in the path for the "riders for the bottle" went a double file of men and women, dressed in all the finery they owned for a great day of merrymaking. The women were gay in their best red, blue, or butternut yellow petticoats and short gowns, with kerchiefs about their shoulders. Here and there gleamed a brooch, a buckle, or a ring, carefully cherished heirlooms. Here and there a dress was graced by ruffles. Some of the older women wore gloves of buckskin and some of them even carried handkerchiefs.

The men wore their hunting shirts, linsey or buckskin fringed in red or blue, leather breeches and leggings, shoepacks or moccasins. Some were bareheaded, but most of them wore their coonskin caps. One or two wore beaver hats, borrowed for the occasion. Some of the men carried rifles slung over their shoulders; some carried horse pistols, which they kept for ceremonies and display; some brought jugs of applejack on their shoulders to add gaiety to the celebration. The horses they rode were fitted out with old bridles, rope halters, broken and mended packsaddles, bags or blankets, and harnessed with string or rope.

"Here they come!" cried the men when they saw the riders. "And it's Jed has the bottle."

"Three cheers for Jed, say I," shouted George, waving his cap over his head.

"And I say three cheers for George, our fair young bridegroom," answered Jed, as he halted his horse and presented the bottle of whiskey to the crowd. "George, you are first. Drink for luck!"

George gulped a mouthful of the liquor and passed the bottle along to the minister, and so it went, down the line until every guest had taken his share. Then back to the best man went the bottle. He drank what was left amid cheers, and the procession then moved on until the cabin in the clearing came into view.

"The bride! The bride!"

Mary Harkin came to the doorstep, laughing and blushing. The guests crowded around her, joking, laughing, pushing, slapping, kissing the sixteen-year-old bride. She was pulled this way and that. She was whirled around so that her new dress might be seen and admired.

The fiddler climbed upon a stump and put his fiddle under his chin. Now the dancing would begin! Two couples took their places and a square dance began with hand clapping, jigging, twirling, and steps weaving in and out, until the fiddler stopped to rest.

The minister, clad in black homespun, sat apart, watching the merriment. At last he called out:

"Stop the music! Stop the dancing! Let the bride and groom come forward."

But there was a shout and a rush, and four husky fellows carried the bride and groom away to the fiddler's stump.

"Jig it off," they commanded. And the crowd shouted, "Jig it off!"

Protesting, George cuffed at the men. Mary laughed nervously. But the fiddler began to play, and the two were forced to begin the jig. They danced until they could dance no longer, then another couple took their places. When they could no longer breathe they were followed by a third couple, and so the jig went on and on.

Occasionally the minister stepped forward and tried to stop the mad jig, but to no avail. It stopped only when the fiddler's arms and fingers ached past bearing.

"'Twill soon be high noon," said the minister.

The young girls circled the bride and gaily led her to the place where the minister stood waiting. The men raised George and carried him on their shoulders, tumbling him at Mary's feet. Jed stood beside him.

"Please attend with becoming solemnity," said the minister. Then he opened his little book with its worn homemade sheepskin cover and read the brief marriage ceremony.

When the wedding dinner was announced—a substantial meal of beef, pork, bear meat, venison, and vegetables, johnnycake, milk, butter, berries, and fruit—appetites were hearty.

On the cabin table, which was a large slab of timber hewed out with a broadax and supported by four rough legs set in auger holes, the bride's family dishes were laid—wooden trenchers, wooden bowls, pewter bowls and plates. There were some crude knives, horn spoons, and pewter spoons, soft and battered. The men used their hunting knives as a matter of habit. The heavy trenchers with steaming meats and vegetables were carried off by the noisy crowd, and three or four ate from one plate, as was the custom.

The men ate heavily.

"We have work ahead of us. No frolics and junketings for us. We've a house to build!"

"Show us the place, George," they commanded. "Is it in the valley?"

"Of course," said George laughing. "You know, everything comes to the house down hill. The place is a mile away, and I filed my claim at Winchester, so it's all right and proper."

"Unless the Indians come and tell you your corn patch belonged to their great grandfathers," said Gil.

There was a short laugh, but this was too true to be funny. Gil regretted his words. No one wanted to remember that there were unfriendly Indians about.

The men rode down the valley to the clearing that George had made in felling the logs for his cabin. Four men were selected as corner men, to notch and place the logs. Certain ones hauled the logs into position by the use of chains. Others split them into boards, or puncheons, for floor and roof, and with their frows, or cleaving knives, prepared shingles and staves.

By the end of the afternoon the logs were raised in position, the stringers were laid and the floor boards were put in place over them. On one side the logs were sawed out for a doorway, and the cut ends were held fast by upright boards. At the end of the cabin an opening was cut for the chimney.

By this time the women had come down the valley, bringing baskets of cold venison and bear meat, johnnycake, honey, and maple syrup for the evening meal.

"You've worked hard enough," they cried. "Come have some supper."

Mary caught at her husband's sleeve.

"Look!" she said, pointing toward the woods. "Who's that?"

A strange horse and rider came into the clearing. The man sat watching the crowd as he rode up to it.

"Will you share our supper, stranger?" called George, amiably.

"What's goin' on here?" asked the man gruffly.

"Logrolling and house-raising for young George Teagarden here, that just got married," explained Jed Lewis, stepping forward.

"I'll talk to this George Teagarden," growled the stranger.

He dismounted.

The men gathered together in groups, listening.

"Are you the fellow that's buildin' this house?" he demanded, looking at George sharply.

"Yes, I am. Why?" asked George.

"How come you're building it on my land?"

"Your land? I rode over to Winchester a month ago and filed my claim with the justice there."

"Well, I can't help that. I took this claim by tomahawk right, nigh two years ago, and I don't see how you can claim it. I'll show you the marks on the trees."

George said nothing.

Mary's heart sank. She had heard of men staking claims by "tomahawk right." They made notches on trees to signify ownership. Sometimes land was sold under such rights. It was not legal, and yet it had not been proved illegal. It was recognized in many places as a legitimate claim.

"If you scotched the trees, stranger, you must have scotched them high and wide. I've never seen the marks," said George, indignantly.

"Tomahawk claim is no good around here, stranger," offered Jed Lewis.

"Where I come from, tomahawk right is as good as any," declared the man.

"How can we settle this?" asked George. "Here's my house already raised!"

"We can go to the nearest justice and let him settle for us," suggested the stranger.

"Nearest justice is forty miles away."

"Well," said the man, "I don't aim to let you settle on my claim without a scuffle!"

"Now there's an idea, stranger!" George stepped forward with alacrity. "We'll fight it out, and the best man gets the land."

The man looked at George narrowly.

"It's agreed," he said at last.

The two men took stock of each other. George was short and thickset, and he had strong legs and shoulders. The stranger was tall and loosely built, but his movements were quick, and his grip, George found, was strong as a bear trap. Frontier life and work had given them both a rugged strength and great endurance.

They selected the most level spot they could find. They stripped off their hunting shirts and threw aside their knives. Then they stood facing each other, waiting for Jed to give the word to start.

Jed motioned the wedding guests to stand away, and they formed a half circle around the two contestants, excited and apprehensive.

"Ready! Go!" cried Jed.

George threw himself at the stranger's body. Quick as his action was, the man was alert and side-stepped, at the same time landing a blow on George's head, behind the ear towards the nape of the neck. George fell, rolled on his back, and tried to rise. But the man ran at him and jumped. George rolled aside, leaped up, and bounded away. The stranger twisted to his feet and faced George, just in time to receive a hard blow on the jaw, which caught him off balance and forced him backwards. As he hit the ground George fell on him. Choking, gagging, gasping for breath, the man was barely able to roll over to escape the scissors grip that George was trying to hold. The stranger was doubled up on his side, unable to move.

George had no wish to lose his uppermost position. He held on. Both fighters breathed heavily, awaiting an opportunity to catch the other off guard.

The wedding guests stood tense and silent.

At regular intervals the stranger made an attempt to shake off the grip that held him. Finally with a sudden jerk and a quick roll the man broke away. George vainly tried to regain his hold. Both men leaped to their feet. There was a sickening thud. George went down, but as the stranger rushed he crouched and tackled. Over and over they rolled. Now the stranger was on top.

One of George's arms was pinned under him; the other was being slowly forced back. His struggles seemed useless. Suddenly he gave a desperate kick and threw his opponent off. Now George was on top. Again he had the stranger in a scissors grip. Slowly his hold tightened. The man grew white around the lips.

"Enough?" asked George, panting with the strain of his exertion. But the stranger shook his head.

George strained his muscles tighter. Every cord and sinew grew taut, every vein throbbed, his skin glistened with sweat. His throat was parched.

The stranger's face flushed with his resistance. His head fell back. His body relaxed.

"Satisfied?" asked George.

"Yes," groaned the stranger.

The crowd cheered. They gathered around the two men, giving them whiskey, offering water when the fighters spat blood from torn lips.

Mary came forward.

"Let me do this," she said; "I will wash your cuts and bruises."

George took the stranger's arm.

"Come into the cabin," he said.

"You've won it, fair enough," said the stranger, "the land, and the house. I'll clear out!"

"But first you must eat with us," insisted George and Mary.

They took him inside the cabin and soon the guests were including him in the merriment. The fiddler struck up a new dance tune and the stranger joined in the jigs. He drank a health to the bride and groom. He teased the girls and talked with the men about politics and farming.

As the moon lifted its silvery circle above the clearing moccasins stamped, hands clapped, and linsey skirts swirled to the music of the wedding festivities.

"Here's health to the bride! Here's health to the groom! And thumping good luck and big children!"

The toast went around. It was the best wish they could utter. Strong sons on the frontier meant help with the heavy work, protection from the Indians.

"Thumping good luck and big children!"

The stranger gripped George by the hand.

"I've another claim a few miles to the south," he said, "and if my rights hold there, we'll be neighbors!"

·[11]·

Dr. Connolly Keeps His Word.

Y ou shall be captain commandant of the district of West
Augusta," said Lord Dunmore, governor of Virginia.
Dr. Connolly's eyes glittered.

"Pittsburgh," continued Lord Dunmore, "will be the county
seat of this district of West Augusta."

Dr. Connolly left immediately for Pittsburgh and lost no time
in taking possession of Fort Pitt. Since the fort had not been in
use for some time it needed repairs, and when everything was in
order he boldly renamed it Fort Dunmore.

"What is this all about?" wondered the Pittsburgh settlers. For
weeks during the spring of 1774, in the cabins along the rivers
or in the streets men gathered to discuss this new turn of affairs.

Virginia had always sent money and armies into western Pennsylvania during the French wars. Now Lord Dunmore openly
claimed the region for Virginia: all the southwestern lands
lying below the Ohio River. Those settlers who had come from
Virginia enthusiastically approved Dr. Connolly's measures, but
the Pennsylvania settlers could not understand it. District of
West Augusta! They laughed.

"Most of that territory belongs to the Shawnee Indians," observed Arthur St. Clair, an official of Pennsylvania's Westmore-

land County. "There's going to be trouble if the people of Virginia aren't careful."

Dr. Connolly—captain commandant of the district of West Augusta—not only took possession of the fort, but he defied all Pennsylvania law and authority. And he commanded—*commanded*—the settlers of western Pennsylvania to assemble as militiamen under the authority of Lord Dunmore.

The storm broke at that. The mutterings of the Pennsylvanians turned into protests; protests turned into violent debate. Violent action would be the next step in this intolerable situation.

Arthur St. Clair acted first. He ordered Dr. Connolly arrested and bound over, to keep the peace. Then he reported to Governor Penn of Pennsylvania.

The governor sent Lord Dunmore a draft of the Pennsylvania boundaries, but Lord Dunmore refused to be convinced by a piece of paper. He wanted that territory!

Dr. Connolly, paroled by the sheriff, promised to surrender himself for trial when the court should meet in Hannastown. After reporting to Lord Dunmore for instructions he returned to his post at Fort Dunmore.

The Pennsylvania justices resented the sheriff's release of Dr. Connolly on parole. Little good it was to lock up a man if the sheriff of the county could free him on a promise!

The three local justices, Devereaux Smith, Æneas Mackay, and Andrew McFarlane, called upon Sheriff Proctor, and the four men went to the fort to talk to Dr. Connolly.

A score of farmers and traders stood listening to Dr. Connolly as he read aloud letters from Lord Dunmore.

"So His Lordship tells Connolly to continue to hold the fort in the name of Virginia," commented Smith.

"He seems not to consider the fact that Connolly has been arrested by the Pennsylvania authorities," said Mackay.

"Listen!"

Dr. Connolly read the second letter:

" . . . to muster the militia in the name of Virginia . . . "

"Arresting the man has done no good," declared McFarlane. "Here he is with the same orders! Sheriff, this man should never have been allowed parole."

The sheriff frowned, but just as he was about to reply Dr. Connolly folded the letters and beckoned to the group of justices.

"Gentlemen, if you will step with me to the barracks, I shall acquaint you further with His Lordship's ideas," he said condescendingly.

"And we follow his orders," marveled Mackay.

In the barracks, Dr. Connolly motioned the sheriff and the justices to a bench alongside the table.

"Gentlemen, since the Hannastown incident I am your paroled prisoner. But I am a citizen of Virginia and loyal to my governor. I have, at his orders, called together the militia and read them his letters. I have no intention, however, of taking any step contrary to the rules of law until I have made good my parole. I beg you to believe that I shall appear at your court and answer to its charges."

Devereaux Smith spoke for the justices:

"We respect your peaceful intentions, Dr. Connolly. As justices of this county our intentions are peaceful, unless in our own defense we are forced to take harsh measures. We have certain duties to perform. We believe we have been lenient. We have honored your word. We hope you do not expect us to neglect our civil duties."

Dr. Connolly replied that he had no such thoughts.

"Court meets one week from tomorrow in the Hannastown courthouse," stated Sheriff Proctor.

"Gentlemen, I shall be there," said Dr. Connolly, smiling and bowing.

"He's just mocking us," remarked Mackay, as they left the fort.

Next morning the town was scandalized to hear that Sheriff Proctor had been seized and thrown into the guardhouse of the fort on a king's warrant issued by Dr. Connolly.

"After all his fine words of peaceful intentions and promises of maintaining law and order," cried Smith in shocked dismay, as he and Mackay met.

"He must have had the warrant all ready when we were with him."

"I don't like this business," said Smith in disgust. "I'll be glad when the court meets."

"But now can we believe Connolly will come to court?" questioned Mackay.

All week this question ran in the minds of the justices. Even when, on the sixth of April, court met at the log courthouse at Hannastown there was talk of Dr. Connolly and his high-handed methods. Would he appear?

All morning the justices in the log courthouse heard cases brought by the settlers—the theft of a pig, the assault of a neighbor, the drunkenness of a good-for-nothing fellow. All morning the justices settled disputes, ordered fines to be paid, meted out punishment: forty lashes, to be given at the whipping post over the bare back of one offender; jail sentences for others.

At noon the court adjourned to a room at Mr. Hanna's tavern, where the justices partook of a dinner of roast young pig, boiled beef, a fine roasted goose, with several bottles of Arthur St. Clair's fine claret brought for this occasion. Again the talk turned to Dr. Connolly.

"Well, gentlemen, is this our last court to sit in Hannastown? Do we submit ourselves now and forever to the laws of Virginia and the commands of Mr. John Connolly?" asked St. Clair.

"Never! Never!" cried the justices.

"What I can't understand," said Devereaux Smith, "is Lord Dunmore's idea that Pennsylvania lost its rights to the Forks and the surrounding country when the French seized the fort. The British troops recaptured the fort, so Lord Dunmore says the title reverts to the crown. And Virginia is a crown colony, so they must have what belongs to the crown. What I want to know is, where do the Pennsylvania settlers come in?"

"They only live here!" exploded St. Clair. "Lord Dunmore is land-crazed. He wants land, land, and more land—so he can sell it and line his pockets with gold. And Mr. Connolly, although he has his imposing title of captain commandant, is Lord Dunmore's land agent and nothing more."

"Gentlemen," interrupted McFarlane, "I seem to hear a disturbance outside, and I have no doubt it is the amiable Dr. Connolly, come to answer his parole."

One of the men went to the door.

"It's Connolly all right. And he's brought a mob of ruffians with him!"

"He wants to be sure of justice," St. Clair observed ironically.

The justices walked to the courthouse and found it surrounded by a cordon of mounted frontiersmen armed with rifles and tomahawks. Sentinels stood defiant guard, and Dr. Connolly himself blocked the doorway.

"Gentlemen," he said, and his voice was hard and insolent, "there will be no session of court this afternoon. I have a message to deliver. Where will you hear it?"

Since the militia so obviously controlled the courthouse, the justices indicated Mr. Hanna's tavern.

Dr. Connolly lost no time, but spoke his message:

"I am here," he said, "not to bring about disturbances, but to prevent them. I have raised this militia to support the authority of Virginia. I am the authority of Virginia in this district. I came here only because I promised to do so. Legally my arrest was impossible, and legally any court held here is unauthorized. To prevent confusion, however, I shall agree to your acting in a judicial capacity until I have instructions from Lord Dunmore or the crown itself. I shall be pleased to have your remarks in writing."

Dr. Connolly strode from the tavern.

The justices were speechless with anger. It was some time before they could write their reply to this autocratic pronouncement. Finally they sent word that the answer was ready.

"Let them come to me with their message!" directed Connolly.

"I would rather cut off my toes than walk to that man," said St. Clair explosively.

"St. Clair," said Justice McFarlane, "will you look out that door toward the courthouse and tell me what you see?"

St. Clair looked and said nothing.

The militiamen.

Two hundred of them, armed and defiant.

"We have no choice," said McFarlane. "Let us swallow our chagrin for the present. This affair is not ended."

Dr. Connolly knew that with his militia as a protection for

himself and a menace to the justices he could have everything his own way. When the justices appeared at the courthouse door he deliberately kept them waiting. They were helpless in their wrath. The sentinels stood guard at the door.

At last Dr. Connolly ordered the justices to enter.

The written reply was laid before him.

Arthur St. Clair spoke for the justices:

"The jurisdiction of this court and its officers rests on the authority of the province of Pennsylvania. His Majesty himself has confirmed it in council. We have exercised that authority with regularity, and shall continue to do so. However, this court wishes to preserve the public peace. Every effort will be made to accommodate any differences that may have arisen between the province of Pennsylvania and the dominion of Virginia."

Shouting and waving their rifles and tomahawks, yelling and hooting derisively at the court and the onlooker, Dr. Connolly and his militiamen rode triumphantly out of the town.

The justices returned to the tavern.

"The blasted Tory!" sputtered Mackay.

"They'll rue their dealings with that tyrant," said Smith. "His Majesty the Captain Commandant!"

"There is trouble ahead," said St. Clair. "However, tomorrow the court will resume its business. Gentlemen, let us wash away the taste of this day with a glass of claret." He raised his glass and waited for the others. "Here's a health to drink: Gentlemen, the province of Pennsylvania!"

And so it was to be, for later events proved that Dr. Connolly had had his inning and it was agreed that the disputed territory was to remain forever under the jurisdiction of Pennsylvania.

·[12]·

The March for Freedom

AT THE door of his cabin a few miles north of Hannastown Christopher Burkett stood looking up the narrow road that disappeared over the top of the hill. Travelers along that way were few, but now came a man in buckskin breeches and woolen waistcoat, a rifle in his hand.

A woman appeared at the door, shading her eyes as she followed her husband's gaze.

"It's Simon Fletcher," said Christopher, as the man drew nearer. He waved his arm in greeting.

"Where you heading with that rifle?" he called.

"Seen any bears?" laughed Simon.

He waited until he came within speaking distance, then he explained, "I'm on my way to Hanna's tavern, Chris. There's to be some action and I want to know what's going on."

Christopher frowned.

"I declare, Simon," he said in exasperation, "these are hard times to live in. The trouble I had, clearing a piece of land for a home. Then the Indians. I don't know that I'll ever forget my own particular fight with them here in this cabin. And then Virginia had to send that John Connolly to start trouble!"

"Wonder whatever happened to him?" asked Simon.

"A man told me he's back in Virginia with Lord Dunmore. And may he stay there, blast him!"

"They found out it was no laughing matter when they stirred up the Indians," said Simon.

"I wish they'd settle down and have a little peace," returned Christopher.

"But now it's more important than ever, Chris. It's our liberty we've got to fight for. It's all the colonies together!"

Christopher looked off to his fields of grain.

"We're too far away, Simon," he said. "When we're in trouble the assembly sits in Philadelphia and does nothing. We fight off the wolves and the bears. We fight off the murdering redskins. We fight off Connolly. We fight off the Mingo and Shawnee Indians. And the assembly lets us fight. Then the assembly says 'Kindly come and help us.' Why? Why should we?"

"Come along to Hannastown, Chris. Maybe you'll find out what it's all about," urged Simon. "An express passed my place yesterday. It seems the British army killed six of the inhabitants of a place in Massachusetts and the New England men—four thousand of them—surrounded twelve hundred of the king's men in Boston.

"Sounds like rebellion, Simon. But that's a long way off. Is there danger of such things around here?"

"Three ships are expected to bring soldiers to Virginia to keep folks in order."

"I'll come with you, Simon. Maybe I should know more about all this."

"We can't keep out of this, Chris," said Simon earnestly. "It's our future that's at stake. It's our liberty!"

The Hannastown meeting stirred the frontier settlers to a

high pitch of excitement. When Arthur St. Clair rose to read the
resolutions the assembled frontiersmen had drawn up for adopt-
tion, men cheered and waved their hats. Then they listened with
rapt expressions and hearts that beat heavily. Some of the phrases
rang again and again through Christopher's mind:

"... animated with the love of liberty ...

"... to maintain and defend our rights ...

"... a wicked Ministry and a corrupted Parliament ...

"To arm and form ourselves into a regiment or regiments, and
choose officers to command us in such proportions as shall be
thought necessary . . . "

Christopher listened carefully. Now they were getting to the
rules and orders.

"We will, with alacrity, endeavor to make ourselves masters
of the manual exercise, and such evolutions as may be necessary
to enable us to act in a body in concert: and to that end we will
meet at such times and places as shall be appointed . . . "

"I don't like this," said Christopher. "It's armed insurrection.
It's cutting ourselves off, independent of the government. It's
overthrowing the king and parliament."

"Probably should be overthrown, when they do us wrong,"
answered Simon shortly.

The voice read on:

"Resolved, that on Wednesday the 24th of May, 1775, the
townships meet to accede to the said Association, and choose their
officers."

The two friends turned homeward, talking over the new
trouble and the pledge to fight.

"It sounds right and proper when they're all together, talking
and excited," said Christopher, "but when you get away, you

remember your home and your land. It's the little fellow that gets hurt. It's his bones that get broken. It's his home that gets burned. It's his land that's destroyed or taken."

"But Chris," argued Simon, "it comes to the point where you have to take sides. An honest man can't keep out of it."

"No," said Chris, sighing. "I guess not."

The two men parted: Chris to return to his cabin and Simon to take a path that led him farther in the rolling country.

.   .   .

In the light of the table candle, a large square of crimson silk lay unrolled. A small British flag lay beside it. On a sheet of paper a man was making a rough drawing.

"Yes, sir," said Colonel Proctor, "that's a fine snake; put thirteen rattlers on him, one for each province. Those rattles will give fair warning. And let his fangs show. You see," he went on, holding up the paper for the other men to view, "on that crimson square of silk the women will embroider this rattler, ready to strike."

"There ought to be a motto," suggested one of the men.

"Let's write below it, 'Don't Tread on Me.' That will be fair warning."

"Now, gentlemen," put in Arthur St. Clair, "since we are not declaring ourselves independent of Great Britain, since we have expressed our loyalty to His Majesty for so long as we are permitted our rights, I propose that we add to our standard His Majesty's flag, under which we have so far lived and intend to live as long as we can."

There was some dissent about this opinion, but at last the small British jack was pinned in the upper left corner.

"I must say," continued St. Clair, "it will be a handsome standard for a newly recruited company to carry. And it would be unthinkable to march without a standard," he added.

"Now gentlemen," said Joseph Brownlee, "let us add initials for John Proctor, First Battalion, Westmoreland County, Pennsylvania."

"That's a lot of initials," pointed out the colonel.

The news spread quickly that Colonel Proctor was recruiting a regiment in Westmoreland. The settlers were not decided about their allegiance. Many adhered to the king and the crown. There were rumors that Connolly was scheming to win the Indians to the king's service. There were rumors of a Tory plot, in which Connolly was also concerned, to raise forces from those loyal to the king and march them to the British stronghold at Detroit.

"The traitors!" Simon Fletcher said vehemently. "And then they'll march down from Detroit to raid western Pennsylvania—men we know. To fight against us! Our own neighbors!"

Later in the summer Chris went to Simon's farm and rode across the wheat field in which his friend was mowing the grain.

"What do you suppose has happened at Pittsburgh?" he asked. "Captain Neville has come from Virginia and taken charge at the fort."

"I know Neville," Simon answered, leaning on his scythe. "He might have orders from Virginia, but he'll carry them out as a loyal American. He's no Tory."

"With the British at Detroit, the Indians west of us, and Tories all through the settlements, I feel as if I can't close my eyes night or day," said Chris.

"Well, when we're needed, my rifle won't be rusty," declared Simon.

Christopher rode off, mulling over in his mind the things he had heard.

Congress planned to raise a Continental army under General Washington. Some of the old Virginia fighters impetuously went east to take up arms under their former commander. The cause of the patriots suffered in the West because of indecisive or hostile settlers. Questionable schemes were afoot with the royalists. Dr. Connolly was arrested in Frederick, Maryland. Papers in his saddle showed clearly that he had been plotting with General Gage of the British army. By now the Pennsylvania and Virginia partisans had called a truce to their antagonisms and united in the defense of their liberties. Virginia's court, however, still controlled the country west of Hannastown, even after Dr. Connolly's arrest, and it was to be some time before the region was handed over to Pennsylvania in a compromise settlement.

A year passed. There was a call for every able-bodied man to enlist in the Continental army. Colonel Æneas Mackay was organizing the Eighth Battalion of Pennsylvania troops, with seven companies. The frontier must be ready for defense.

Steadily the men reported.

Simon Fletcher made himself a new pair of buckskin breeches and a pair of stout brogues, and his wife knitted him a good woolen vest. His rifle was clean and ready. With Christopher Burkett and other volunteers, he went to Kittanning, where the regiment was stationed. For weeks the men marched and drilled, learned to obey orders, learned precision. There was not a uniform among them, but they kept their rifles clean and bright, for they might need them at any moment. Not one in six had a second outfit of jacket and breeches, moccasins or shoes. They had bearskins for warmth, or woolen blankets. As winter came on, they built rude shelters of logs. Six hundred men faced the cold without complaint. They ate their scant provisions stoically. They slept under straw when the snow fell on their faces through the cracks in their rude huts.

The end of the first week of December, 1776, brought orders to move east. Philadelphia was in danger. General Washington was in dire straits.

"But what about the defense of the West? Kittanning is the point that the British must take first if they come from Detroit through Erie. What about our homes? Leave them unprotected?"

"What about equipment? Uniforms? Blankets? Food? It's a long walk to Philadelphia!"

More than one man deserted, to go back to his farm to defend his own family, his own property. At the beginning of the new year grimly silent men took up their guns, strapped their blankets and rugs over their shoulders, and trudged eastward mile after mile over the old trail through the wilderness. Their ankles grew stiff, their feet grew numb with cold. The ice and stones cut into their moccasins, and later when snow fell the leather became wet and slippery. When a halt was called wood had to be collected for fires. The flames scorched the men's faces and the cold froze their backs. They slept with their feet to the fire, drying their moccasins, thawing their frozen bones.

"Simon, it doesn't make sense," complained Chris. "Why do we do this? Look at us, all miserable and suffering, and only a few days from Kittanning. We won't live to see the Delaware River."

"You'll feel better tomorrow after you've had some sleep and hot tea in your stomach," replied Simon. "Whoever expects a soldier's life to be a bed of roses?"

The cold continued, and at cabins and farms along the line of march the men gathered up straw and carried it with them for cover and bedding. They foraged for game: turkeys, partridges, squirrels. They stuffed straw and dried leaves inside their hunting shirts—anything for a little extra warmth. Leaves and straw kept their feet from the wet spongy leather of their moccasins. Mile after mile those moccasins must travel. One hill after another must be doggedly conquered. The longer and steeper ascents told the men they were crossing mountains. The snow drifted knee deep, waist deep. The wind was bitter cold.

On and on the army marched for six days. The day's march was shorter, now, for from time to time men fell in the ranks, exhausted, hungry, chilled, fainting.

"Chris," said Simon, as the army encamped by the roadside on Sideling Hill, "you've scarcely said a word since morning. Are you ailing?"

"Ailing? Maybe you could call it that. I'm sick of this marching to defend the East, when our own frontier needs defending. Not a man here knows whether his family is alive. And what can a lot of buckskin skirmishers do against those British redcoats?"

"We'll show those redcoats something, if it's only our rags and our frozen feet," said Simon.

Day by day the snow fell. The broken columns struggled forward. Supplies ran out. Corn cake, baked hard at the campfire, was not enough to give heat and strength. The men were feverish and delirious. Every day the army was diminished by death or desertion.

The twelfth night Simon woke with a start. Chris had gone!

Simon crawled from his crude shelter. He quietly made his way down the trail. Against the snow he saw a dark figure headed for

Men fell in the ranks, exhausted, hungry, chilled.

the woods. Simon, too, left the road. It was all he could do to keep Chris in sight as he stumbled from tree to tree. He pushed forward, but his feet felt heavy. His breath came unevenly.

Chris was deserting.

But he mustn't.

By a strenuous effort Simon reached him.

"Chris, you can't do this. Come back!" he cried.

"Simon, get out of my way. This is my affair."

"You are not going home, Chris. Unless it is over my dead body," declared Simon, taking hold of Chris's rifle.

"See these feet," said Chris. They were wrapped in straw, straw that was matted with frozen blood. "See these clothes." They were rags and tatters. Knees and elbows showed through the holes. "Look at those men back there in the snow. Feet wrapped in rags they've torn from their jackets. And every one of them bent double with hunger!" His voice shook with a sob.

"Are my feet any better than yours? Are my clothes any better than yours? All I have fit to wear is my woolen vest." Simon opened his jacket and pulled at the vest, which already was looking worn.

"It doesn't make things better, Simon, knowing everybody else's miserable. Shoot me, or let me go home." Chris sank listlessly into the snow against a tree.

Simon threw down the rifle. He took off his coat. He pulled off his vest and put on his coat again, stuffing it with leaves.

"Get up," said Simon.

Chris sat, unmoving.

Simon stooped over him, tugged and pulled at his jacket until it came off, drew the woolen vest over his shoulders and with great effort got the jacket on him again.

"Now Chris," he said gently, "you can go home if you want."

He waited a moment, then started back to the camp and the fire. He had not gone far when he heard limping, stumbling footsteps following after him.

"Simon," called Chris. "Simon!"

Silently the friends made their way back to the fire.

.   .   .

A cabin or a tavern or a settlement was a welcome sight along the road. As the army reached the eastern settlements people came out with spare clothing, caps, jackets, a blanket, outworn shoes to offer the straggling line of men stumbling by. Food was offered to the hungry, protection and care to the sick.

Near the Delaware River they were met with shouts and cheers.

"Washington has been victorious at Trenton and Princeton. Philadelphia is safe!"

The news spread warmth and fire through the ranks. As bravely as they could, the ragged Eighth Pennsylvania Regiment marched through the streets of Quibbleton, New Jersey. Now they would be part of this army under General Washington. Now they would share in the shouts of victory. Their rags would be changed to uniforms of the Continental army. They would sleep in barracks. They would eat.

The two friends walked to the officers' hut at the end of the camp. Inside, at the table, they were given a paper:

"I do swear (or affirm) that I renounce and refuse all allegiance to George the Third, King of Great Britain, his heirs and successors; and that I will be faithful and bear true allegiance to the Commonwealth of Pennsylvania as a free and independent State, and that I will not at any time do or cause to be done any

matter or thing that will be injurious to the freedom and independence thereof, as declared by Congress . . . "

Christopher felt a lump in his throat. He had no doubts now.
He could accept this oath of allegiance. He looked at Simon and
nodded his head.

At the bottom of the paper they wrote their names:

"Simon Fletcher."

"Christopher Burkett."

· [13] ·

Indians in the Valley !

A HOT midsummer sun beat down on the village of Hannas-town in the fertile valley. It was Saturday, and the women and children busied themselves with prepara-tions for the evening supper. The fires from the midday meal had been left to die, but thin curls of smoke still rose from the chim-neys of the thirty log houses scattered around Robert Hanna's tavern. There a few idle men sat smoking and drinking, talking over the merits of their cattle, boasting of their good farms.

"They're cutting wheat today at Michael Huffnagle's place," contributed John Guthrie. "I should be there. Michael's anxious to get his wheat in before there's a storm."

"Sun too hot for you, John?" asked John Steel, puffing con-tentedly on his pipe.

"Can't seem to get my strength back, after that fever I had in the spring," explained Guthrie. "Today I'm left behind to watch over the bread-baking," he laughed good-naturedly. "Every-body's gone but the littlest youngester and me." He knocked his pipe against the arm of the chair. "Maybe I'd better take a look at that bread."

"You don't live so far but you could smell it if it burns," said Steel. "I must go back to my place, though, and do some hoeing.

There's always plenty of work to do on a farm."

Guthrie looked in the oven at his wife's bread. He wondered about his little boy, but the shouts of children playing somewhere around reassured him. Picking up a bucket he walked toward the fort to get fresh water from the spring.

The heavy gate of the stockade hung open. Within, at the clear spring in the middle of the yard, stood a girl in homespun lin-sey. Her black hair was brushed back from her forehead and bound with a blue ribbon. She smiled and nodded to John Guthrie, then lifted the water bucket she had just filled and looked toward the interior of the fort.

"Jamesy," she called. "Where did ye get to?"

From behind an old barrel came a mischievous giggle. A curly-headed boy bounded from his hiding place and came running across the court. John Guthrie laughed.

"He's sturdy, for a youngster three years old," he remarked. "Playing pranks already! I can see he keeps you busy, Margaret."

"That he does!" said Margaret, but she looked at the child fondly, and laughed as she took him by the hand and led him out of the stockade.

Margaret Shaw was the favorite of every settler in the valley. She was sixteen, strikingly handsome. Of all the young men who wanted to marry her, she considered only one: Richard Miller. He was a stalwart youth of twenty, handsome in a rugged, straightforward way that, with his courage and his energy, had taken her heart. But Richard himself was not to know this. He kept hoping, asking—and knew nothing of her choice.

"Why doesn't he say something about Jamesy?" Margaret wondered. "I can't desert Jamesy. I've looked after him since he was a baby, since the day his mother and father were killed. I couldn't give him up! He belongs to me. If Richard loves me, he will take Jamesy too."

Frontier tragedies gathered strange names and faces into families. The bitterness of life made men cling to one another for courage, for help, for protection. Waifs and stray children were taken in and cared for, names were lost and forgotten. These things were taken for granted. No doubt then Richard also took it for granted. She would think no more about Jamesy . . .

Abruptly, a shout broke into her thoughts. She heard the pounding of a horse's hoofs, and leaped up, startled. She ran to the door just as the figure of Sheriff Matthew Jack appeared on his great black horse.

"Indians!" he yelled. "Indians!"

"Where, Matt, where?" asked Guthrie, clutching the bridle of the prancing horse, his voice betraying his excitement.

"Back of Michael Huffnagle's! One of the harvesters saw them. It's a war party creeping through the woods. Warn everybody! I'm off to spread the alarm." Sheriff Jack wheeled his horse and was gone down the road.

"Indians!" whispered Margaret.

"It's four years since we had an attack. That was the time Eve Oury risked her life to save the garrison and drive the Indians away," answered Guthrie.

"I wish I could do something like that!" cried Margaret, her courage rising.

"The thing to do is to get everyone into the fort," said Guthrie. "Round up everyone you can." He ran over into his own house and gathered up the newly baked bread.

"Everybody to the fort!" he shouted as he ran to the farthest houses, up and down the streets.

From the fort the harvesters could be seen hurrying through the fields. What possessions they could they carried into the yard of the fort. They drove their cows and horses before them. A place was provided for the livestock away from the people. Michael Huffnagle, carrying the county records, took command and gave orders briskly. Rifles, ammunition, food! These must be gathered from every home, quickly. Women and children must be protected. Families must be gathered together. Everyone must be accounted for before the gates were closed.

John Guthrie looked everywhere for his little boy.

"Have you seen Johnny? Have you seen my boy?" he asked right and left.

The women shook their heads, clutching their own children to be certain of their safety.

Guthrie rushed out into the village.

"Johnny," he called. "Johnny!"

The last stragglers squeezed in through the gate. It was only open a few inches now, and several men were stationed close by to shut and bar it at the first sign of the Indians.

Scouts must go out. Young men who could go quickly—Richard Miller, David Shaw, the Brison twins volunteered to go at once. Margaret's hands were cold. She looked at Richard.

"Margaret," said Richard in a low voice.

"Will ye go scouting too, Richard?" Her voice faltered.

He bent and kissed her.

"Good-by, Meg," he whispered.

He went quickly to the spring with his three friends, hastily deciding which directions they should take. The twins to the west. Richard and David to the north. They separated and circled the village. Avoiding the open farm lands, Richard and David kept to the woods toward Crabtree Creek, The water of the creek flashed silver through the green bushes, but they did not notice. There was a thrashing noise in the underbrush and suddenly Sheriff Jack on his black horse loomed before them.

"Run for your lives, boys!" shouted the sheriff. "The Indians are yonder by the creek. Here, grab my stirrups."

The boys each seized a stirrup and started toward the fort in great leaps. The speed of the horse almost seemed to give them wings.

Three warriors appeared on the other side of the creek. At sight of the three men they started in pursuit.

Every second David and Richard expected to hear the crack of a rifle behind them, to feel the sharp flash of pain from a bullet. They leaped over logs and gullies, they crashed through bushes. Could they reach the stockade? There was no sound of close pursuit. Had they outrun the warriors? Had the Indians given up the chase? When they reached the open road into the village David looked behind him.

No Indians were in sight. A few steps more and they would be safe inside the stockade. David must pass by his own house. In a flash, he remembered his proudest possession: a fine buckskin jacket, worked in elaborate beading. He hesitated, then let go the stirrup and dashed into the house through the open doorway. He pulled the coat from its peg.

Back at the door he stopped short, breathing heavily. A tall Indian was aiming his rifle at Richard and the sheriff, who had almost reached the stockade gate. With a quick movement David raised his own rifle and fired. The Indian fell.

Now the way was clear. David dashed for the gate and was safe. Richard ran to him.

"I thought you were with us all the time," he cried.

"That was an Indian right behind you," said David. "If I hadn't stopped to get my fine jacket—well, he might have got you!"

"That was the shot we heard. And you saved my life!"

"It was all because of my fine jacket," insisted David.

"They're going to close the gate," said Richard. "The Brison twins are back, and John Guthrie." His face sobered. "They can't find Johnny."

David looked around the yard. Sixty people had taken refuge in the fort. Twenty were men. Seventeen rifles were gathered together and examined, but only nine were fit for use. Michael Huffnagle gave a short laugh. Nine rifles! Ammunition was low enough, to be sure, but for nine rifles—there was ammunition to spare! The men were divided into two firing squads, to take turns with the rifles. The stockade itself was strong enough to withstand an attack. There was no fear on the faces of the men and women, only a stern determination to stand against these red warriors who threatened the peace of every settler on the western frontier.

"It's Guyasuta with his Senecas and Canadian rangers," said Michael Huffnagle. "They've come all the way from Lake Chautauqua, down the Allegheny River to Kittanning, and then marched overland."

Guyasuta had intended a surprise attack. The man on the black horse had ruined his schemes. Now, under shelter of the buildings, the Indians raided the pasture lots and stables, driving the horses they found into the woods, killing the cattle.

The houses were looted, the few meager possessions that were the pride of the settlers were carried off, or wantonly destroyed.

Occasionally an Indian or a Canadian came within range of the defenders of the fort; then shots rang from behind the stockade. From the houses the marauders opened fire upon the fort.

Ten feet from the gate a section of wall had rotted away. Shot after shot poured through the weak spot, but to no avail. Everyone steered clear of the place and kept out of the line of fire.

Margaret, with the other women, stood near the men, ready to help, to carry water, to reload rifles. Jamsey was with the children. He was mischievous and had his own ideas about the sort of game the men and women were playing. He wanted a rifle too. He darted across the yard, right into the danger area. A bullet struck a swirl of dust at his feet. He stopped and backed away. A second bullet hit the dust. Jamesy was frightened. Not knowing what to do, he stood still, sobbing.

"Margaret!"

She heard the child, gasped with fright, ran and seized him in her arms.

"Jamsey! How did you ..."

She sank to the ground. Pain shot through her breast—sharp burning pain sped through every nerve in her body. Richard and David were at her side. They lifted her from the ground and carried her to the small cabin at the east corner of the fort. The women dressed the wound, but they could not remove the bullet from her lung.

Darkness fell and the Indians gave up their attack on the stockade. The night grew quiet and the summer stars shone bright in a sky of murky blue. A wind came down from the north. The settlers kept watch. Relief might come from somewhere, but there was not much hope of it.

At midnight a house at the far edge of town broke into flame, then another, and another. The crimson flames leaped roaring into the darkness. The Indians capered and danced in the red glare, their moving shadows long and terrifying against the bright background of fire. All attempts to burn the fort were successfully thwarted by the accurate shots of the defenders. But the buildings near the fort burst into flames and Michael ordered every available kettle and jug filled with water to be kept ready for use against flying embers.

"Thanks be, there's a strong north wind," cried Michael. "It blows the fire away from the stockade."

The Indians drew off. Shouts and whoops made the night hideous. Soon they sounded fainter and farther away, as the Indians followed the creek back into the wilderness.

There was no sleep that night for the people of Hannastown. If there were tears for their lost homes and their dearest possessions they dropped silently in the dark, unnoticed.

The morning sun rose on a desolate scene. Of the thirty log buildings only two remained: the courthouse and the cabin nearest the fort. The rest were ashes.

Were the raiders gone? Would they come back?

Sheriff Jack rode into the country to learn what he could and to get supplies. Everywhere he went the Indians had killed and plundered. Survivors straggled into the fort. Late in the day young Isaac Steel limped into the yard, pale and exhausted.

"I leaped a rail fence," he said. "Then I crept through the thick brush in a roundabout way. I saw the flames and hid."

"And your father?" asked John Guthrie.

"I don't know. I saw him jump from a window and run. But I don't know where."

The misfortunes of other settlers did not banish from the minds of the Hannastown people the tragedy of Margaret Shaw. In spite of care and kindness and all the medicine available, Margaret died, her hand in Richard's hand.

"She told me she wished she could do something brave and heroic," said John Guthrie, "and then—she saved Jamesy. Now the child's alone, I'd like to take him, if nobody would mind. He's not so much younger than my own little boy—that's lost."

.   .   .   .

For several weeks the scouts patrolled the country and then it was reported once more safe for the settlers.

But Hannastown was never rebuilt. The ashes were carried away by the summer winds to mingle with the dust of wheat and corn fields, and plows and harrows turned up the earth, breaking land for new farms where once stood the cabins and log homes.

·[14]·

Elder Smiley Volunteers

THE pastor was on his way to church. He settled the gray beaver more firmly on his head and gripped the worn Bible under his arm, walking with even, deliberate steps along the footpath through the fields and woods. Behind him, following in his steps, were his wife, dressed in her best gray gown and bonnet, and the children in their homespun.

The pastor knew his thoughts should be on his sermon, but he found himself thinking more and more heavily these Sunday mornings about his family, his farm, his congregation—and money. Life was becoming very difficult.

"Five years," he meditated. His thoughts went back even further in distance and time, and he saw himself a student at Princeton, living in an attic, studying his Greek Testament, with high ideals of service to humanity, with abiding faith. The bread of life! He wanted to offer it to everyone. He wanted to devote his life to teaching and preaching.

"Martha," he said, turning to his wife, "it's been five years—do you remember—since we came here to Washington County."

"I'll not soon forget that, Joseph—the long trip it was, with the children, and the house things tied on the horses' backs."

"And the wildness of the country," said the pastor.

"It's still wild," replied Martha, "but at least we don't have to plow and reap under armed guards keeping watch for Indians. Those were the bad times. Even now we don't know that our beans and our wheat won't be burned to the ground."

"Aye, but we must have faith," sighed the pastor. "We'll have a good harvest if the weather holds. It's been a good year. But more than a good harvest is needed to pay what is due on the farm to Angus McCray, and there isn't any money."

Martha was silent. No one knew better than she how little money there was. For three years the congregation had been unable to pay the pastor's salary, in spite of good harvests.

"There's too much wheat," she said. "It doesn't pay to sell it, you get so little. The last pack train that went to Cumberland had to barter twenty-one bushels of wheat for one bushel of salt. What can we do? We must have salt. And we can't raise wheat to give it away."

"But we can manage to get along," said the pastor, "if only I can rid myself of the debt owing on the farm."

"There will be a way, Joseph," said Martha, but her voice lacked conviction. How often had they tried to think of a way to earn the money to pay Angus McCray!

The pastor remembered how eagerly he had signed the deed to the acres of timberland on Buffalo Creek. Angus McCray had said to him, "And what name do ye give this tract, parson?"

"I shall call my new lands 'Welcome,' in remembrance of the petition that my people have signed, calling me to their church," he said. "Two hundred settlers!"

"Renegades and outlaws, no doubt," observed McCray.

"I am not unmindful of the frailty of humanity," rejoined the pastor.

"And I found the people in the backwoods no worse and no better than the people in the East," he reflected. "Gossip, slander, petty abuses and wrongs, quarrels and jealousies—they are everywhere."

He loved the people of the frontier, and if his mind were at rest about the security of the farm "Welcome" he would gladly devote his whole life to his congregation, to serve them and to help them.

He had found them eager to accept law and order and righteousness, and, although they were scattered as far as thirty miles apart, they were in other respects a united and compliant people. They brought him their questions and doubts, their trials and troubles. Many nights he had prayed for them, leaving his bed and kneeling on the rough puncheon floor. He had been with them in their joys and in their sorrows—rejoiced with them and mourned with them. Yes, he loved the frontier people—realized it more than ever now that he was faced with the prospect of leaving them.

A wood pigeon flew up through the dense foliage into the blue of the sky.

"Listen!" said Martha. "He's calling. It's just as if he flew up to Heaven with our prayer."

They stood in the sun-flecked shadows and heard the strange, sweet song of the bird flying overhead.

Through the path in the woods came groups of men and women walking and riding from their cabins in the valley. The log walls of Upper Buffalo Church were visible through the trees. The women and children who were walking went to the creek to bathe their bare feet and put on their Sunday shoes. Shoes were not to be worn over rough roads, ten miles to the church, so it was customary to carry them until the church was sighted.

The clearing around the log cabin was crowded. The men in their buckskin hunting shirts stood hatless in the sun, their coonskin caps under their arms, their rifles slung over their shoulders.

"Parson's thin looking and worried," said Alex Moore, the miller.

"We've got to do something," said Elder Morgan, "or first thing we know we'll have no parson!"

"Parson Smith's a good man. He won't blame us for his troubles. He knows we've no money," said Kirk, the tanner.

"Maybe he has thought of something," suggested Elder Morgan. "What will we do if we can't keep our pastor? Who's going to marry us? Who's to bury us?"

"That's right! We've got to keep him somehow."

"The place wouldn't feel right without parson!"

The murmur of voices died as Reverend Smith guided his tall thin body through the aisle to the pulpit. Every face was raised to the pastor. The men who could not get inside the church crowded around the door, for the pastor had a power over these people. His voice rose and fell with the earnestness of his message. When he prayed he asked for counsel in the time of crisis, for the preservation of the congregation he served, for more perfect faith. Before the congregation was dismissed the pastor announced that there would be a special meeting on Monday evening to discuss ways and means.

When the assembly met the next evening the claim against the pastor's farm was the main discussion. Plan after plan was offered and turned aside. A committee had waited upon Mr. McCray at Pittsburgh. Alex Moore, the miller, Mr. Kirk and Mr. Graham,

They heard the strange, sweet
song of the bird flying overhead.

the tanner and his partner, and Reverend Smith himself had all talked to Mr. McCray.

"He is as obstinate as Shylock himself," declared the pastor. "And he will not barter. He will have money—gold pieces, in fact."

"But there's not a gold piece in the whole countryside," gasped the women.

Could the women bring what coins they had, brooches and gold chains, rings and bracelets, to send off for exchange or to have melted into bullion?

In all Buffalo Valley there was not enough ready money to pay for a good team of oxen, and certainly not enough jewelry to fill a teapot.

"All we have is our wheat," said the miller.

"I'll do this," said Alex Moore; "send me your wheat and I'll grind it into flour free, if I can do it between my regular jobs. From my mill it can go to Buffalo [*Wellsburg*] and from there to New Orleans."

"New Orleans!"

"I'll give fifty bushels of wheat!" said Elder Patterson. "My south field will yield more than thirty bushels to the acre. I can spare fifty."

"I'll send a hundred," offered Henry Graham. "I gave the land for the church, and I want to keep the pastor in it."

"I'll make the casks," said McEwen, the cooper, "if someone will help cut and soak the staves and hoop poles."

"A hundred bushels is more than I'll get from my whole sowing," said Thomas Olden, a young farmer from Mill Creek. "I've no horse, either, to carry it. But I can offer ten bushels."

"My son and I will fell and shape the logs for the boat if those with teams of oxen will meet to drag them to the river," volunteered a farmer with a good stand of timber on his lands.

A carpenter and a neighborhood handyman agreed to construct the boat, and several boys volunteered to caulk the seams if the carpenter would show them how it was done.

On and on it went. Enthusiasm spread. There was not a member of Upper Buffalo Church but was ready and willing to help save the pastor's farm. By the end of the session the boat and casks had been provided for as well as enough wheat promised to make five hundred barrels of flour. A committee had agreed to wait upon Angus McCray and obtain his promise to wait for his money until the flour was sold.

In a month the wheat was gathered and ground and ready for shipping. Weeks of labor had produced a flatboat with a cover for shelter and portholes to serve in case of attacks from the Indians. When the flour was ready, the great flatboat was ready.

"Who will run the flour to New Orleans?" The Reverend Smith stood in his pulpit, and his voice rang with confidence.

The boat was built and moored, ready for its cargo. The flour was stored and ready for loading. But no one had offered to run the boat down the two-thousand mile stretch of unknown river, through uncharted waters, sand bars, snags, perils half guessed, dangers fully anticipated.

The church was silent. Tall, strong men who had battled with Indians for their lands looked at the pastor and said nothing. Young men who had acted as scouts and had cut their way through dense forests, had hunted bears, and were adventurous and fearless, thought of the strange and hostile country, and were dumb.

"Who will run the flour to New Orleans?" The voice challenged again.

The dark interior of the church seemed filled with some fearful menace. The people sat rigid with expectation. The women hardly dared breathe. The men glared stonily at the wall before them. It was too great a task; it was too great a sacrifice.

But the boat was moored at the bank.

The barrels of flour were waiting at the mill.

"Who will run the flour to New Orleans?"

In a darkened corner, where women and children were packed together on the hewn log benches, there was a rustle and a sound of indrawn breath.

Old Father Smiley, the elder, rose to his feet.

"I will go," he said.

There was a murmur of excitement. Was he able? Was he strong enough? Could he handle a boat?

"But I shall want four younger men to go with me," continued the old man.

"What of our families? What of our farms?" each man asked. "We can't afford to lose our crops."

"Pay the men out of the proceeds. That's fair enough," suggested Elder Morgan.

Now more than one young man listened to the discussion. The farm losses would be covered by a sum of money paid the young men on their return.

"I'll go," finally volunteered a youth leaning against the wall.

"And I," came a voice from the opposite side of the room.

Two others quickly volunteered.

Hands reached out to the volunteers. The pastor's eyes filled with tears. Perhaps this was all for him, but he hoped it was for the life of the church, for the sake of religion, for the cause of Christ.

The pastor's wife began to sing. She had a clear voice and she sang from a thankful heart. Another voice joined hers, then another, and another, until the whole congregation had joined in the psalm, and the clearing rang with the sound of triumph.

.   .   .

The mists rose along the Ohio River one cool morning of October. Elder Smiley and his companions with some of the other men from the congregation had loaded the flour into the flatboat. Venison, pork, and other provisions had been stored for the weeks of travel. Gunpowder and bullets had been supplied. The crew had spent many an hour overhauling their rifles and sharpening their hunting knives. Now everything was ready.

Friends and neighbors began to arrive at the river bank. James Edgar drove some of them in his wagon, as did Elder Marquis and Elder Graham. Some came on horseback, wallets of food hung over their saddles, last minute offerings for the three voyagers. Scores walked the long dusty miles from their homes in moccasins or in their bare feet. They inspected the boat, counted the barrels, stood by the green river bank, and called out to friends.

"There's parson," said Elder Smiley, clearing the deck of people. "He'll give us a prayer before we go."

The pastor was ardent and grateful for the work that had been done; his perfect faith in the success of the voyage filled the congregation with confidence, the voyagers with courage.

Elder Marquis lined out the stanza of a psalm:

> My Shepherd will supply my need,
> Jehovah is His name.

The people felt the significance of the psalm. They repeated the lines:

> My Shepherd will supply my need,
> Jehovah is His name.

Louder grew the voices, rapt, hopeful, and exultant, needing no leader.

> In pastures fresh He makes me feed
> Beside the living stream.

When the last note echoed from the hills Elder Smiley stood at the cable ready to haul, his gray head bent over the heavy knot. Every eye strained to see the boat take the water.

"Untie the cable," called the pastor; "we wait the Lord's will!"

The boat swung out into the current of the river, and a tremendous shout followed it. Hands waved, handkerchiefs fluttered, and the congregation stood on the bank until the boat had disappeared around the bend in the river.

"We wait the Lord's will," they said, their hearts full.

. . .

The corn and pumpkins had been gathered in. Autumn deepened into winter. The men went on hunting trips. At home bacon and hams were cured and beef was smoked. Hung from the rafters, the meat smelled sweet in the smoke of the cabins. When snow fell and the streams froze the men busied themselves with patching moccasins and making new shoepacks, molding bullets, chopping wood, and repairing farm implements. In every cabin the whir of wheels told that flax was being spun into linen thread. Sometimes wolves howled from the edge of the forests.

Winter snows deepened; then with February the first thaws opened the ice on the creeks.

All winter prayers were offered for the safety of the five voyagers. The long months passed without the least trace of news. The mild warm air of May blew over the valley, and the flowers of the wild plum grew fragrant.

Eight months had passed.

Angus McCray said his patience was exhausted.

"At the end of June I'll take back the farm," he said. "Reverend Smith will have to do what he can."

The Reverend Smith and his family still kept days of fasting and prayer. But men passing the open church and hearing the voice within felt that prayers were useless. Hope for the travelers' return was fading.

Stories of other travelers' experiences were recalled, tales of hardship and horror, accounts of days of starvation and sickness, of dazed wanderings in the marshes, of poisonous plants and snakes, of Indian warriors who surprised the hapless traveler at night, robbed, and killed him. Men began to wonder at what particular spot in the savage-infested wilderness Elder Smiley and his young men had met their tragic fate. No, there was no use praying.

The last Sunday in June brought a sober-faced congregation to Upper Buffalo Church. The long winter had been lonely for many, and the Sunday services offered the people a brief period of companionship. They went to church that Sunday wondering how they could manage without the pastor, wondering where the pastor would go when his farm was taken from him. That day he would give them their last Communion.

They entered the church with sad expectations. In the dim

light, in his place on the hewn log bench sat a strange, yet familiar figure. Could it be possible?

Elder Smiley!

As if he had never been absent a day, Elder Smiley sat composed and meditative, waiting for the Communion service. This was no day to talk business. Holy Communion.

"The Lord has prospered our voyage," he said simply and looked up attentively at the pastor.

The pastor's hands shook as he opened his Bible. His eyes filled with tears, but he did not need his eyes to see the text he already knew by heart. His voice rang strong and clear, it rose and fell with the earnestness of his message. Joy filled the little log church. This was a day to be remembered as long as life lasted.

"I thank God we are home," began Elder Smiley when he told his story at the special assembly on Monday evening.

"Amen!" agreed the people.

The elder made his story brief. He knew the people were not interested so much in his own experiences as they were in the result of the trip. He merely mentioned the delays on the way downstream, touched on the difficulties of managing the heavy flatboat, of running aground, and told briefly of the wide expanse of the Mississippi River, of the vast forests along its course, of the levees and the indigo plantations, of the market at New Orleans.

"We sold the whole cargo of flour, Parson," he said.

A murmur of gratitude ran through the congregation.

"Then," continued the elder, "everything except fire and flood held us back. Indian trickery. Illness. We doctored one another with herbs. Lying on beds of leaves . . .

"We bought a horse to carry our provisions and bags, and the horse galloped off with all our possessions, including the money for the flour! The boys caught him at last and recovered the money, but that money made us uneasy wherever we had it! Indian guides proved treacherous. They stole our hats, our largest kettle, and a gun. They suspected we had money . . . "

The narrative went on and on. The briefest outline of nine months of hardship and privation. At last the elder was silent.

From the floor he lifted a great leather wallet and laid it on the table.

"Parson," he said, "we sold the wheat at the top price—twenty-seven dollars a barrel."

He turned the wallet upside down on the table. Into the yellow sunlight poured a great pile of gold money. Gold pieces! More than any of the congregation had ever seen in their lives.

It was unbelievable! It was a dream made true by a glint of sun. It was an old man's tale somehow real and unreal at once. It was a miracle performed before their wondering eyes. Their mouths gaped open. They rose and pressed forward to see. Children climbed up on the benches. Boys clung to the rafters to look over the heads of the older people.

One hundred dollars were counted out to each of the crew. They went forward to put the money in their pockets and pushed their way back through the people, flushed and embarrassed. Such wealth set them apart from the rest of the congregation.

Reverend Smith looked at the old man beside him.

"What are your charges for the trip, Father Smiley?" he asked.

"Well, parson," he said meekly, "the young fellows did all the heavy work. I don't ask for any pay."

"Give Elder Smiley double pay!" said Alex Moore.

"Triple pay!" shouted Elder Marquis.

"No, no! It was God's work," protested Elder Smiley. "I should ask no reward were it not for the loss of my summer wheat. Just the same as the others, I'll be glad to have."

The good elder was voted three hundred dollars of the money.

"This money was brought from New Orleans for the pastor, not for me. I'll not touch it until he has what is rightfully his," declared the elder.

Never was money more joyfully divided. Bright gold coins to pay him his salary for a year to come. The pastor smiled, but he could not trust himself to speak. He stood as if in a dream.

Every farmer who had given wheat for the flour received a profit on his investment! Every debt was paid. Hearts were light, minds were free.

The barrels of flour and the gold coins became a legend in the valley. Some people called them a miracle—a miracle of faith and prayer.

"It was parson who never gave up," they reminded each other. "It was parson's faith."

Liberty and Learning

T HE byre was cool and fragrant. Young Hugh Brackenridge sat on his three-legged milking stool and adjusted
the pail between his knees. On the straw near by, just
within range of his eyes, he laid his book, open at the fourth ode
of Horace. He leaned his head against the cow's flank as he
milked, and his eyes followed the black print down the page.

Through the doorway the early summer sun changed the morning dew to sparkling jewels. Along the last hill of the York County
barrens, beyond the cabin, lay clouds of early morning mist.
Outside the door a blackbird was calling from the cherry tree.

This was the time of day and the chore that Hugh liked best.
Awake with the first pale streaking of dawn, comfortably fed
on bacon and cornbread and milk, he could have an hour with
his book, unquestioned and undisturbed while he milked the
cows. It was much better than grubbing stumps to extend the
clearing. It was more pleasant than burning brush and laying
rails for a new stretch of worm fence.

At this hour Hugh Brackenridge was not a pioneer boy helping
his father and mother wrest a living from the barrens. He was
not the son of the family that, arriving in Philadelphia in 1753
after a three months' voyage from Scotland, had been obliged

to sell their surplus clothing before they could continue their way west to take up land and raise their log cabin; he was not a linsey-clad boy of thirteen living under the harsh Calvinistic doctrines of a settlement of dour Scotch axmen, not a boy attending the school at the junction of Scott's Run and Muddy Creek.

With the Latin cadences of the odes of Horace sounding in his ears, he was a herd boy in ancient Italy milking his goats in the shade of an ilex tree, watching for a dryad to appear, hearing wood nymphs, fauns, and satyrs call to him through the ivy and the myrtle leaves. The boy who lived in daily apprehension of Indians found delight in the idylls of Rome; listening to the song of the blackbird, he heard instead the magic lyre of Amphion.

Lessons in Latin and Greek for a farmer boy on the western frontier! Lessons from the clergyman, in exchange for which Hugh performed certain chores. But what were a few chores to pay for a new world, a world of beauty and richness?

When his pail was full Hugh closed his book and led the cows out to pasture. From beyond the apple orchard came a clear, sweet call, a succession of musical notes like chimes.

Hugh set down his pail and placed his book carefully on a stump near by, vaulted lightly over the fence, and walked softly under the trees to find the bird. Down in the ravine he looked, through the dense tangle of vines and underbrush. The jerking movements of the singer revealed his hiding place.

"It's my yellow-breasted chat," the boy thought. "It's come back again!" He gave a low whistle and the bird twisted this way and that but was not frightened away. Once again it sang its sweet cascade of notes, flirted its tail, then flew jerkily deeper into the ravine.

Hugh went for his pail and his book. And suddenly the morning sun seemed dulled. Life dropped to its lowest ebb. The little gray book was gone.

Hugh searched everywhere. Then he looked up, horrified.

"Bess," he cried. "Bess, how could you!"

He wrenched the precious book from the cow's mouth. She had already chewed some of its pages, and the shreds fluttered on the grass like the petals of the cyclamen Horace described; the book was wrecked past all further reading.

"Oh Bess!" wailed Hugh. "I walked thirty miles to Fagg's Manor for that book last Saturday and thirty miles home again on Sunday. And now look at it. Ruined! And I'll have to take it back, Bess. What will Reverend Blair say to me?"

Bess turned her back and unconcernedly munched clover.

"I'll pay for it somehow," thought Hugh, "but the worst of it is, it's gone and I've nothing to read."

That was the calamity. For the rest of the week, until he could walk to Fagg's Manor and have another lesson in Reverend John Blair's study, he would have nothing to read but mutilated pages. He pounded his fist on the fence rail rebelliously.

"Books! I want books!" cried Hugh Brackenridge.

.   .   .

The school at Gunpowder Falls was a typical frontier school, a log structure of one room lighted by a window of glazed paper, with a fireplace for winter warmth. A few logs glowed on the hearth, for the first autumn frosts had chilled the valleys. Most of the pupils were barefoot, and the heat felt good to them. They sat on benches, facing the walls, muttering aloud the lines set out for their lesson.

The master looked at the backs of his pupils. At his side was a bundle of hickory withes, but for three days he had kept order without using them.

When Hugh Brackenridge had walked up to the door of the log school with his books, his quills, and his ferule under his arm, the pupils had taken him to be one of themselves. They had been astonished when he took his place at the tall desk in the front of the room.

"Books!" he had called to them, and in amazement they had given him their attention. The schoolmaster!

Schoolmaster. He was only fifteen, two years younger than his oldest pupils. For the children who were learning their letters in the horn-book Hugh had no misgivings, but he anticipated trouble with the obviously amused oldest pupils, the girl in green linsey who at seventeen was ready to be married and the brawny, big-jawed farmer boy who sat near her. Unless Hugh could master them he could never be master of his school.

There was a titter at the back of the room and Master Brackenridge went quietly over to assert his authority. Over the shoulder of the farm boy he caught a glimpse of a drawing: a baby in a high chair sitting at the master's desk, a bottle in one hand, the master's quill in the other.

Hugh reached for the drawing, but he was not quick enough. The big fellow jumped from his seat and waved the picture in the air. The pupils laughed: the boy was half a head taller than the master.

"Dave Gillison, go to the desk and show the school what you have done."

Nothing could have pleased Dave better. He swaggered to the master's desk and held up the drawing for the school to see. There was a shout of laughter.

The young master walked to the desk.

"Now," he said, "we shall see who laughs last."

With his hard right fist he struck at the boy's head. The pupils gasped. Dave struck back, and the pupils rose in a body, ready to take his part.

"Go it, Davy!" they cried.

The young schoolmaster stood his ground. From the hearth he seized a burning brand and with one blow laid the fellow on the floor at his feet. Then he turned to the rest of the school.

"Back to your places!" he thundered. In a moment all was quiet.

"Who laughs last?" he demanded of Dave.

"You do, sir."

"Go to your seat then."

That night the boy appealed to the trustees, and Master Brackenridge was called upon to explain his indignity to young Gillison. Hugh told his story and was confirmed in his actions.

"We have faith in you, Master Brackenridge," said the trustees. "It is not an easy work, this teaching."

Young Master Brackenridge nodded his head.

"I want to do a lot," he said. "I'll teach them everything I know. But there is so much more to learn!"

.　　　.　　　.

September 25, 1771. Autumn sunlight shone softly on the walls of the College of New Jersey in Princeton, spreading over the green grass of the college lawns, and lingering on the laughing faces of the men who were promenading along the walks with young women in rustling silks. It was commencement day, and presently the graduates and their friends would listen to long and tedious declamations pronounced with all the solemnity of youth. Hugh Brackenridge would deliver the Latin salutatory, *"De Societate Hominum."*

Hugh was sorry his college days were over. All too short had been those four years of Latin and Greek, history, philosophy, and mathematics. He had acquired a brilliant reputation in oratory and debate. He was known for his wit, his verses, and his prose satires even as far as Philadelphia. Young Philip Freneau was his classmate—Philip, whose poetry reflects the spirit of the young American nation and still lives on. James Madison, who became president of the United States, and William Bradford, a famous lawyer, were also Hugh's classmates. They had all been members of the Whig literary club and had spent long evenings writing satires against the Tories.

Liberty and learning—those were the ideas that their minds turned upon. Those were the ideas that would prepare the way for civilization in the new country. Philip and Hugh had written a long poem about *The Rising Glory of America,* telling of its discovery, its settlement, its frontier warfare, agriculture, commerce, and science, with prophetic hints of great achievements in the future.

As Hugh read this poem at the commencement exercises he was loudly applauded:

> 'Tis but the morning of the world with us
> And Science yet but sheds her orient rays.
> I see the age, the happy age, roll on
> Bright with the splendours of the mid-day beams,
> I see a Homer and a Milton rise
> In all the pomp and majesty of song,

Which gives immortal vigour to the deeds
Achiev'd by Heroes in the field of fame.

The morning of the world! Hugh Brackenridge carried away from Princeton the desire to help build a new world.

.　　　.　　　.

Westward over the old York road Hugh traveled, his law treatises and his books in his saddlebags.

At Pittsburgh he established a law practice and with the passage of years became one of the leading citizens of the western country.

.　　　.　　　.

Hugh Brackenridge's home looked across the Monongahela River to the green hills beyond, and the river breezes wafted the fragrance of roses through the open windows as he waited for his friend, Nathaniel Bedford. While he waited he mused upon the country he had made his home, on the town that was becoming more a gateway to the western country and less a frontier village. He thought of his hospitable and talented French friend, John Marie, whose tavern on the hill above Pittsburgh was famous for the stimulating company to be found there. Hugh had missed much in his western home—a culture, a refinement, a broader life, glimpsed in his college days, but now experienced only in his books. His son and his friends' sons should know and value that culture, should have more than a tavern on the hill, he promised himself.

From his window Hugh saw Dr. Bedford approaching.

"Bring the baby down, nurse!" he called from the door of the room he used as his office. "Dr. Bedford is here."

Baby Henry cried lustily.

"I can't say that you have produced a handsome young man," commented Dr. Bedford, smiling at the crying baby.

"He'll do well enough," said Hugh, "besides it's his ideas that will matter. If his ideas of liberty and learning are sound, he will be handsome enough!"

"Still harping on liberty and learning," smiled the doctor. "We've pretty well settled the young man's liberty for him. We've got our independence from Britain. As for the rest . . . " The doctor waved a hand around the room, where a desk, a secretary, and a table held books in English, French, Latin, and Greek.

"This is not enough," insisted Hugh. "By the time he can read these books there will be hundreds of others published. Every month sees some new idea developing. We brought ideas with us from other countries. We had teachers who knew what was going on in the world of ideas. They knew books. They knew people. I wouldn't take all the farms on the frontier for my days at Princeton and the ideas Witherspoon gave me. And these French books—some day you'll see, Rousseau and those others will have a tremendous influence in our country as well as in their own."

"You and I, Mr. Brackenridge, will be under the sod when that happens."

"But my son won't be, doctor. Here we are, cut off from the cultural world on the other side of the mountains. We have the first thing a man must have—land to call his own. But the next important thing is education. The education of our boys. There's Neville's son, and Stephen Bayard's, John Ormsby's, Tannehill's, and all the rest of them. What are we going to do with them when they're ready to think? We have to get ready for them, doctor."

"Mr. Brackenridge, when your son is able to reach for these books on your desk we'll see what can be done for all the young people," said the doctor. "And in the meantime," he added, returning the baby to the waiting nurse, "give him warm milk with a few drops of lime water in it."

Hugh laughed.

When the doctor left Hugh took up his walking stick and set out through the streets, his mind absorbed with an idea. It was like a spark that grew with startling suddenness into a blaze of light. He walked along Water Street toward the hill. The day was pleasant, the breeze from the river was fresh and cool. At the corner of Cherry and Water Streets he turned and walked toward Ewalt's field, where he paused.

There was a log building in which boys were being taught the elementary branches of learning.

Hugh Brackenridge looked at the structure with critical eyes.

"A coonskin academy," he thought. "That was all very well for the old frontier, for the old days of buckskin clothing and coonskin caps." He looked down at his plum-colored breeches and coat, his silk stockings, his buckled shoes. The rough frontier clothing of early Pittsburghers was fast being replaced with finer apparel. "And the coonskin academy ought to be replaced also." Hugh pounded the ground with his stick. "A coonskin culture will not suffice for gentlemen in broadcloth and linen. I shall not be satisfied for Henry Brackenridge to have a backwoods education. No, something must be done!"

He walked beyond the Greentree Tavern and went to Robert Galbraith's house.

"Mr. Galbraith, will you come with me to Mr. Duncan? I have a plan I should like to discuss with you."

Mr. Galbraith consented, and the two men walked toward the tavern.

"Pittsburgh will not always be a backwoods village, Mr. Galbraith," began Hugh. "But this school is not enough to develop the great men we need here. Look at Henry Lee of Virginia, Livingstone of New Jersey, Adams of Massachusetts. Those men were not educated in schools such as this."

"No, sir," agreed Mr. Galbraith. "Those men were university men.

"Exactly. Now I contend that an eastern university, such as the University of Pennsylvania, is not the least service to one out of five hundred of our western population. We cannot support our children three hundred miles from home."

"I am sure that I cannot," confessed Mr. Galbraith.

"Then," said Hugh, with a deep breath, "don't you see, we must establish our own university."

"A big venture," said Mr. Galbraith, shaking his head.

"But a grand venture, isn't it?"

"But—universities are not founded on air. Where is the money?"

"There is still much land here," explained Hugh. "Three thousand acres could be sold across the Allegheny—in lots—for an endowment that would support our university."

The two men entered the Greentree Tavern.

"Has word come from Mr. Kimzer?" asked Hugh of the host.

"We expect him within the week, sir, if the weather and the roads continue fine. Mr Scull is in his room."

"Ask Mr. Scull to come down," said Hugh, and turning to Galbraith he explained, "Mr. Scull is to print our newspaper. And a newspaper will help us in our plans."

When John Scull appeared the three men made themselves comfortable at a table with three glasses of negus before them.

"I never thought I would set up my print shop in a backwoods village," said Scull, laughing, "but here I am, thanks to Mr. Brackenridge's persuasive powers. And do you know, subscriptions are coming in steadily, though we have to take our payment in chickens, pork, whiskey, flour, and potatoes." He laughed good-humoredly. "Money is scarce in this country."

"At least you won't starve," Hugh assured him.

"Have you decided on a name for the new paper?" asked Galbraith.

"*The Pittsburgh Gazette.* Mr. Kimzer is bringing the press with his load of freight. It's small but will do for a beginning."

"We are together in a momentous venture," said Hugh.

"I doubt it not, sir," agreed Scull.

Hugh Brackenridge launched into his favorite theme: liberty and learning.

"We shall make history by making men," he said. "The printed word is a powerful light, a light that will fill men's minds. It is a force that molds men's wills and guides their actions. The *Gazette* will harness the destiny of this western country to that of the great East, and we shall in turn become great. Now then, we must put our press to good use. I propose that you carry a plea in its earliest pages, sir, for an academy to be set up here in the town. By creating sentiment for such an undertaking we make possible the fostering of an institution whose greatness will precede and determine the greatness of the new country. We shall, on the tide of this favor, apply to the assembly at Philadelphia for a charter. Our sons, even our daughters, will grow in the light of two great ideas—education and liberty. Such an institution will foster religion, which the common people here sadly need. It will be favorable to liberty, for it will mold men's political opinions. It will promote just ideas of law and government, and it will be friendly to the promotion of the manners of civilization. And I doubt not it will encourage agriculture within this region, and manufacturing."

"If you write in the pages of the *Gazette* with such persuasion, sir," interrupted Galbraith, "you will turn men's minds inevitably toward our scheme."

"I am glad you say 'our scheme,' Mr. Galbraith. It must be ours —the idea of all the frontier people for a full and free life. When it takes such hold in each man's mind that he calls it 'our scheme' its success is assured."

The room grew dark with evening shadows, but the men talked on. Candles were brought. One by one other men of the town were summoned: John Wilkins, John Gibson, Stephen Bayard, Presley Neville, Dr. Nathaniel Bedford.

In the candle-lit room the men sitting at the table or standing by the windows were fired with the fervor of Hugh Brackenridge's words. Those men could look ahead. They were not content to live just for the moment. In all earnestness they filled their glasses to drink a toast to the new academy.

"Mr. Scull," said Hugh, as they moved toward the door, "we'll scatter the pages of your newspaper over all the western counties, and they shall stir the western people to raise here a great institution of learning."

"One week ago," said Scull, "on my arrival here, I saw only a squalid backwoods village of paltry log houses and streets of mud, with dogs, hogs, and cattle roaming at will, with uncouth men lounging about, traders coming and going—a place with two doctors and four attorneys, a few merchants, and a school teacher. But this evening I see other things, Mr. Brackenridge." Mr. Scull paused, and a new light came into his eyes. "I see a great city spreading out on all sides of the rivers, climbing the hills, filling the valley . . . "

"Mr. Scull," exclaimed Hugh Brackenridge, "we shall do this thing! It is not a vision; it is a plan for the future! Not one of us can choose but go forward."

When Hugh returned to his home he took the lighted candle from his office, mounted the stairs, and went into the room where the baby lay asleep in his crib. He leaned over the child.

"For you," he whispered. "Liberty—and learning!"

·[16]·

Whiskey Rebels

LEN THOMAS and his neighbor, John Harmon, looked out over the rolling farm lands west of Mingo Creek and gloomily shook their heads. The young rye showed delicately green against the dark rim of pines edging the pasture. A light breeze went through the fields in rippling waves.

"That's fine rye," Len boasted. "Makes the best whiskey hereabouts."

"Too bad we have to turn that good grain into whiskey, Len," commented John. "But there's no use trying to tote such heavy stuff over those rough mountain roads to the Philadelphia or New York markets, and you can't get any money for grain around these parts."

"Well, whiskey's as good as gold, here and in the East, too, John. I trade mine for all sorts of things—salt, and tea, and knives, and bullets, and even a couple of new saddles here the other day. Yesterday my wife took a gallon down and got some fancy spices . . ."

"Ho!" interrupted John. "My Amelia traded some for a new winter bonnet. Cost less whiskey than eggs, she said!"

"Come over and see my still," Len invited. "I've got things fixed a new way." Then his face sobered. "I don't know that it

189

pays to keep fixing a still up now, with this new law. A man has to register his still, then pay for a license to operate it or pay a tax on the whiskey itself. I'm a law-abiding man—I thought I'd pay the tax before an exciseman got a chance to knock at my door— but I'm pretty upset about the whole thing."

"I never thought we'd see an exciseman in this country," said John. "I've heard my father tell how people hated them in Ireland."

"They're hated here, too," broke in Len indignantly. "One of the excise officers was tarred and feathered down by Mingo Creek."

"That sounds like the work of Tom the Tinker," said John.

"Tom the Tinker! Do you think he really is a person?"

"You'll be pretty sure he is if you get one of his letters."

"Oh, I think it's just some wild young men out playing pranks," declared Len.

"Expensive pranks," pointed out John.

The friends skirted the field of young rye and followed a path only faintly discernible through the apple orchard beyond the pasture. The wild blackberry bushes caught against their coats as the ground sloped into a ravine deeply shadowed and tangled with heavy underbrush. The smell of soft black earth mingled with the musty, unmistakable odor of the still.

Len quickened his steps as they came in sight of the entrance to the still. A scrap of white paper was nailed to the doorframe. He tore the paper off and looked at it.

"Listen to this, John!" Len read aloud:

<blockquote>
You encourage the excise law.

Look to your still.

Tom the Tinker.
</blockquote>

"Tom the Tinker himself!"

Len crumpled the paper into a ball and shrugged his shoulders. But John shook his head.

"It's a warning," he said. "I've heard Tom the Tinker makes trouble for anyone who pays the tax. It's a warning, Len."

"Look here. A warning, you say? John, the still is full of holes. It's ruined!"

Together the men examined the still. It was wrecked, there was no doubt. It was riddled with bullet holes.

"This is what I get for being law-abiding," said Len bitterly. "I paid the tax because a man can't go against the government he's fought for. And a law is a law."

"Things like this aren't going to help repeal the law," said John, soberly. "I'm against violence. We should act within the law."

Glumly the two turned homeward, each thinking of Tom the Tinker.

A thousand stories were told about that man. He was bold and fearless, even forcing the *Pittsburgh Gazette* to print his warnings to individuals. Some people claimed to have encountered him in person, but only a few followers had proof of his identity. Everyone knew the wandering tinkers who traveled from place to place with their solder and iron, prepared to mend pots and kettles and farming implements. Tom the Tinker called himself by that name because he "mended" the farmers' stills by shooting them full of holes. "If you do not oppose the excise law Tom the Tinker will call and mend your still," was a common warning.

.   .   .

On the same day Len Thomas discovered his "mended" still

David Bradford, prosecuting attorney for the county, received his Philadelphia mail. He opened the newspapers and settled down to read. Suddenly he flung the newspaper into the open fire and watched the pages scorch with heat. A burst of flame caught at the edge and soon the hateful print had blackened to a handful of ashes.

Then he regretted his hasty action. Newspapers from the East were rare in Washington County in the 1790's. They were passed from one hand to another, begged and borrowed, read and re-read.

"Congress might as well disperse," he said to himself. "They've done nothing about the excise law. Mr. Hamilton is all powerful. He does what he pleases. He wanted to rile the West with his tax on whiskey."

Bradford rose excitedly and strode across the room to the table.

"Mr. Hamilton!" he cried, pounding his fist against the pile of law books spread before him. "Mark my word, Mr. Hamilton, you're not going to have your way any longer!"

Pacing back and forth across the room, Bradford thought of the new government, the new laws made in the East, and the Federalists who directed the policies of the country from the nation's capital in Philadelphia. The western counties of Pennsylvania were opposed to the Federalists, whose leader was the highhanded Alexander Hamilton. The "all powerful" Hamilton said he had long since "learned to hold the popular opinion of no value" and openly disregarded the sentiment of the people.

"But *this* time," thought Bradford with a grim smile, "you've gone a step too far, Mr. Hamilton, and you'll take some notice of the people's opinion! We'll let you know we won't stand for your excise on whiskey!"

Acting on impulse, Bradford sat down at the table and began to write a letter of remonstrance against the new law.

Other letters of protest were being written from the western country. Like the first low rumbling of thunder the murmur of discontent spread through town and farm land.

"Why do they have to tax our whiskey?" men demanded. "Why can't those fine gentlemen in Philadelphia find something else to tax? Seems as if the new law is aimed right at us west country people. That Tom the Tinker knows what he's about."

.   .   .

John Harmon rode thoughtfully down the trail from his home near the Mingo Church to Washington, the county seat, where a meeting of protest was in progress. He had hesitated about going, but he wanted to know how the situation was viewed in town.

Groups of men were gathered together talking earnestly and excitedly. One group was erecting a liberty pole. A tall sapling had been stripped of its leaves and branches, and long streamers with mottoes printed on them were attached to its top. "Liberty and No Excise," John read. The men dug a hole for the pole and moved it into place, cheering loudly:

"Down with the excise law!"

John listened to the talk:

"Fifty warrants for arrest sent into the west country! That means fifty men will have to leave their farms and travel to Philadelphia at their own expense, just to be present at their own trials!"

"Why, I'd have to sell my farm to get money enough to go all that way."

"Most of us would. Whiskey is the only money I have."

"Say, I haven't had so much as a shilling in actual money this last year. Even pay my church dues in good Monongahela rye!"

"And the pastor is glad to get that!"

John moved on to another group.

"But what will happen if they confiscate our stills? We'll not even have our whiskey to trade with."

"It'll be fight or starve, then. Bradford's idea is to prevent all that. Obstruct the government."

"Bradford's talking now. Let's listen to what he has to say." The men moved closer to the horse block on which Bradford was standing.

"It's all Hamilton's work," the lawyer was saying. "He wants to show the people the power and strength of the new government. He says no government is firm until its authority has been tested by military force, and he's ready to enforce this law if it takes out the militia of the whole country!"

"Well, then, let them send their army," yelled a hotheaded young man. "We can show them we're *men* not slaves!"

"They'll say we have no right to organize ourselves this way. It's treason to raise an army against the government," someone objected.

"We have a right to assemble peaceably for redress of grievances without having an army called out against us," insisted Bradford. "The government will soon wake up to the fact that the West must be given some consideration when it comes to laws and taxes."

"Bradford's the man to lead us," shouted a voice at John's ear, and there was a murmur of approbation from the crowd. John turned to look into the bold eyes of a youth of perhaps seventeen. "Look," the young man said, pointing out a vigorous, sun-browned farmer. "That's Holcroft. He's Bradford's right-hand man. Some folks say he's Tom the Tinker!"

Holcroft was middle-aged, well dressed, not at all the mental picture John had had of a wild young man. Tom the Tinker? Shooting bullets through stills, robbing gristmills, burning barns —that man? John shook his head and turned again to listen to Bradford.

"I don't favor tarring and feathering or coercion," said Bradford loudly, "but we must be all for one and one for all—at any cost. Effective measures must be adopted!"

John looked again at the men near him. It was impossible to look at most of them and think of lawlessness and rioting. What would an army do against men who had left their guns at home? Men who wanted nothing but a voice in their own government?

"They're right!" he said to himself. "And I'm with them, heart and soul!" He rode away from the meeting with a feeling of great exaltation. "We fought England because of her excise law, and now our own government levies on us the same kind of taxes without letting us have a thing to say about it. Tyranny at home is no easier to bear than tyranny from England!"

He was glad that he had gone to the meeting—he had many things to ponder on the way home. He was almost curt in greeting the two men who caught up with him after the second mile. Then he recognized Bradford.

"We're going the same way," said the lawyer. "I hope you won't mind our joining you." John saw that Bradford's companion was the youth who had spoken to him at the meeting.

"My name's Judd," said the young man.

"Mine's Harmon," said John, and turned to Bradford.

Elated with the success of the meeting of protest, Bradford

talked freely. Almost, John thought, as if he were talking to himself and not to a stranger riding beside him.

"We'll oppose this thing to the last breath . . . We'll show the East . . . We won't stand for their laws being thrust upon us . . . We can be sure of the people, the real democracy . . ."

"How many are with us?" asked John.

"Thousands!" exclaimed Bradford. "Thousands! we have secret organizations, all opposed to the authority of the federal government." He leaned toward John confidentially. "When the time is ripe we'll separate from the government! We'll make our own laws. We'll be independent . . ."

John listened amazed. He had had no idea that Bradford's plans were so bold.

"Of course," he faltered. "The mountains are a natural barrier . . . We are like another country." But his brain was whirling. Bradford would be the ruler of the west country! Wasn't he a little dazzled by a vision of power and glory . . . Suppose he failed? The lawyer would risk much, but the responsibility for his actions would be shared by many.

The voice of young Judd broke in upon John's thoughts:

"We've designed a flag for our new republic. It has seven stars for the seven counties of Pennsylvania and northwestern Virginia."

A flag for a country not yet formed!

"We're going to call it Westsylvania."

John was speechless. Where were the loyal men, willing and anxious, who had promised to "submit to the laws of the United States" and who had given their solemn oath of allegiance to maintain independence and honor?

"There must be some men who can see this thing straight,"

he thought unhappily. "There's right on both sides and how is a man to know what he should do?"

Other people were asking the same question.

As the federal government took measures to put the excise law into effect most of the small farmers refused to register their stills, some of them discontinued the distilling of whiskey, and more and more of them grew bitter to the point of violence. The government tax collectors, or excisemen, were given to understand that they were definitely not wanted in the country. The office of exciseman was considered precarious, as well as contemptible. Then Hamilton, thinking to mollify the westerners, hit upon the idea of appointing General John Neville as inspector of the excise in the Pittsburgh district. He was a man well known and respected in the western counties.

Unfortunately the appointment had the very opposite effect.

"Neville!" exclaimed John. "Why he was one of the earliest objectors to the law. Now he's to enforce it. He'll never accept."

But Neville did accept his commission. Open and violent anger ran from county to county like wildfire.

"Traitor!" shouted the farmers, and the once popular general became an object of hatred. Black looks and muttered curses followed him wherever he went. With the United States marshal, he rode about the work of serving writs against the farmers who had not registered their stills, a duty that required considerable courage. At more than one farm, the two were driven off the property with guns.

Fifty men marched to Bower Hill, the home of General Neville, to demand that he give up his commission.

"Never will I accede to such a demand," declared the general with scorn, and the door closed with a bang behind him.

The crowd was furious. A shot rang out. Was it from the house or was it from the angry men outside? It didn't matter, for that shot resulted in great confusion and firing from both sides. The signal of a horn within the house directed a volley of shots from the negro slaves in the cabins, and this unexpected flank attack wounded six men and dispersed the mob.

Excitement and fury ran rife through the region. The insurrectionists, realizing that small groups were isolated and weak, called the local militia to Couch's Fort, the old blockhouse near the Brownsville road. Five hundred aroused farmers and small distillers appeared at the stated time. It was decided to march on Neville's home immediately.

John Harmon was among those who had misgivings about the wisdom of such action:

"Where's Bradford? Isn't he going to lead us?"

"Bradford is prosecuting attorney for the county; it's better for him to stay away. He'll be able to help us in other ways."

John was dubious. "So Bradford keeps his hands clean, and Major McFarlane is to have the honor, whether he likes it or not." It was obvious that McFarlane was not eager to lead the expedition.

"But Bradford's a lawyer. We need an experienced military man."

"Young boys are needed, too, I see," replied John, as he indicated Judd.

"Why not? Judd's a likely lad. It's his future as well as ours we're fighting for. He might as well know what it's all about."

At the edge of the woods that reached almost to the brow of the hill where stood General Neville's home, Major McFarlane posted his men. The general had a force of soldiers from Fort

Fayette in Pittsburgh guarding the house, and the insurrectionists sent out three men with a white flag to request a parley.

"General Neville must give up his commission as an excise officer."

"The general is not at home," replied an officer from an upper window.

"We don't believe it. We'll search the house for him and his papers!" cried the irate men below.

"We are here to see that you don't set foot inside this house. The excise records are not his. They are the property of the federal government."

The three men reported to Major McFarlane.

"Neville's hiding," growled the men in the ranks. "We'll rout him out!" And the guns of the insurgents flashed and cracked.

From the windows came answering volleys. When at last the firing from the house stopped, Major McFarlane thought the soldiers desired to make overtures for peace. He stepped out to order his men to withhold their fire. At that instant a shot from the house struck him down.

There was consternation.

Major McFarlane killed!

The insurgents redoubled their efforts.

"Storm the house!" cried Judd. But the men hung back.

Judd fashioned a crude torch and lit it by flashing the powder in the firing pan of his rifle. Watching his chance, he crept toward the barn. Then he made a dash and flung the lighted torch into the haymow. A cloud of yellow smoke burst into blinding flame that scorched the rafters and set the roof ablaze. The negro cabins soon caught fire from the barn. A shout from the insurgents spread the news that the roof of the house was smoldering. Soon it too flashed fire, and it was evident that the house would be destroyed.

"Now we've routed them!" yelled the insurgents as the hapless defenders fled from the burning house and surrendered.

"But we don't want prisoners," protested the insurgents among themselves. "What can we do with government soldiers? What'll we do with them?"

"Release them! Send them back to Pittsburgh!"

The men were relieved when the federal soldiers marched off. Those soldiers represented the authority of the United States.

There was no doubt about it. The western country was now in open arms against the law. Treason!

David Bradford arranged for a general meeting at Mingo, and there he advocated a formal declaration of rebellion and continued resistance to tyranny. A Pittsburgher, Hugh Brackenridge, pleaded for conservative measures. He warned the men of grave danger from their recent foray. He spoke plainly:

"Your act might be morally right, but it is legally wrong. It is treason. It is cause for the president to call out the national militia—in fact, it is his duty to do so!"

This statement of fact evoked great concern.

But David Bradford frowned. The persuasive Brackenridge could sway the crowd to his way of thinking. Bradford suspected Brackenridge of being lukewarm in the "cause." Brackenridge and the other men from Pittsburgh talked submission to the law, not insurrection. "Protest against the whiskey law in a legal way," they said among themselves, "but in the meantime submit to it."

"We'll have to hold together in this business," said Bradford to John Holcroft. "I distrust these men from Pittsburgh. I suspect them of spying on us. I'm afraid they send news to Philadelphia, while they talk softly to us at our meetings."

"Yes," agreed John Holcroft, "they were not with us in the expedition against Neville."

On a hot July afternoon bold robbers, muffled to the eyes, stopped the postrider outside Greensburg and forced him to give up the mail to them. Letters written by Pittsburghers were taken out, and the postrider was permitted to go on with the rest of the mail. Bradford received the stolen letters and found, as he had suspected, that five of the influential men of Pittsburgh were denouncing the insurgents and deploring the lawless situation that prevailed in the West.

Bradford raged. The writers of these letters must be imprisoned. They must be captured at once. They were all guilty: Presley Neville, John Gibson, James Brison, Thomas Butler, and Edward Day!

"We'll hang them!" swore Bradford.

Through the Monongahela country went the call for a general muster of the militia at Braddock's Field, August 1. There were rumors of a plot against Pittsburgh.

Bradford planned boldly. The insurgents were to march openly into Pittsburgh, and if the people refused to join forces with them the town was to be burned to the ground. Then they would take Fort Fayette from the government men, and seize the arms and ammunition stored in it. The writers of the objectionable letters would be captured and imprisoned in the fort.

Young Judd told John Harmon confidentially: "We'll sack and burn the town. We'll hang the five men! And then we'll set up our new government."

"Are you sure we have men enough to do that?" asked John.

"Five thousand men will help," boasted Judd.

Five thousand! The town of Pittsburgh numbered scarcely more than a thousand individuals, men, women, and children.

Five thousand men! They came at a word. From all over the Monongahela country, down from the north and up from the south, from the east and from the west they came, grim and determined, to join the rebel army. Some walked barefoot. Some brought greatcoats to sleep under; others came with blankets, Indian fashion, over their shoulders. From Greensburg and Brush Creek, from Rehoboth and Upper Buffalo, from Canonsburg and Washington, from Mingo and Cross Creek, they came with their rifles, muskets, axes, knives.

Every new group was greeted with cheers.

Bradford rode from one knot of men to another, encouraging, advising. It was his hour and he enjoyed to the full the adulation of the crowd.

"We'll show the government that we mean business," he boasted.

"But where are the men from Pittsburgh?" the cry went up. "The regiment from Pittsburgh?"

The shouts were like a challenge.

"They're coming. They're really coming." It was young Judd who spread the news.

It was true. The Pittsburgh men were coming.

They marched across the field amid shouts and cheers. The suspicions of the crowd were allayed. The townsmen had joined with the farmers. Pittsburgh, the very seat of "treachery," had sent comrades in arms, showing itself friendly and sympathetic to the "cause."

The Pittsburghers announced that they had exiled the enemies of the cause, the writers of the stolen letters; hence there was no need of imprisonment and hanging. Seize the fort? That would never do, for the ammunition there was needed for General Wayne, who was fighting the Indians to the west.

Bradford felt frustrated. His fine plot was petering out to nothing.

Brackenridge, determined to break the revolt and to keep under control the dangerous excitement of this army of insurgents, went from group to group, listening, conferring, talking without apparent restraint, but subtly attempting to discourage the men in their plan to march on Pittsburgh. He soon realized, however, that the men were not to be dissuaded. So Brackenridge changed his tactics and pretended to agree with them.

"We must go through with this march," he said emphatically. "It will convince the government that we mean business. We must make a show of force. But it must be without violence. We are a regular army and we must show that we can discipline ourselves. Then we will be respected and listened to."

The talk went on; the campfires blazed. There was little sleep at Braddock's Field that night, for on the action taken the next day hinged the issue of war or peace!

The next morning a Pittsburgh committee rode ahead to warn the citizens that the army was moving upon the town and that every precaution must be taken not to anger the men.

"They will march through the town to the banks of the Monongahela River, where they should be refreshed with whiskey and whatever food is available. All stores and taverns must be closed. Every boat, every ferry is to be collected at the river bank to take the army across to the south side and out of the town at once."

The people of Pittsburgh were in a furore of excitement and fear. Would the army remain peaceful? They did not believe so, and hastily buried their silver, their valuable papers, their money. They brought out what food supplies and whiskey they had, and carried them to the Monongahela River bank. Then the Pittsburghers locked their doors and waited.

Numbers gathered on Coal Hill across the river to witness the descent of the insurgents upon the town. The army could be heard far in the distance. The cavalry swung into the town, then columns of infantry followed in regular formation. The marching men waved their hats and coonskin caps on their rifles.

"Down with the excise!"

"Huzza for Tom the Tinker!"

"Liberty and no excise!"

The columns swung along, two miles and a half in length, people said. On the banks of the Monongahela the ranks broke, and the men gladly ate and drank their fill after the eight-mile march. The hospitality of the Pittsburghers and their apparent goodwill toward the cause satisfied the men that the townspeople were with them. The plan to take revenge upon Pittsburgh was abandoned. The insurgents made their way to the ferries and crossed the river. Those on horses forded the river. By evening the town was well cleared. Pittsburgh was safe.

Bradford, acutely disappointed, nevertheless talked of "a glorious revolution, effected without bloodshed." But his hopes for a new country dwindled and died when word came that the national troops were on their way west. Fearful of the consequences of his leadership in the rebellion, Bradford quietly left the country.

Tom the Tinker made one last desperate appeal, ending with

the threatening words: "Traitors! Take care for my hammer is up, my ladle is hot! Tar, feathers, and burning for any who vote for submission!"

But from the East came the national troops, thirteen thousand strong.

Liberty poles were hastily chopped down. Prominent rebels found it advisable to leave the country—they had been too active in the Neville affair. Their names were too well known. Young Judd disappeared. John suspected that he had followed Bradford to Louisiana, and pictured the fugitives living hunted lives, Judd still loyal to his chief and Bradford recollecting his hours of power as a half-remembered dream.

The day of reckoning came when Secretary Hamilton arrived to question the insurgent leaders. Citizens of Pittsburgh and the surrounding country were called from their beds early in the morning, and marched through the rain to open pens, where they waited miserably for dawn.

"I've been opposed to lawlessness and have tried to prevent rebellion," protested John Harmon when he was questioned.

"You were with the insurgents at Neville's house," was the reply. "Have you proof of your innocence?"

John was silent, helpless, and bewildered as he was pushed into the guardhouse.

Twenty men were taken to Philadelphia for trial, each one walking between two mounted guards, in the cold and melancholy weather of December. On Christmas Day they entered Philadelphia wearing paper cockades to indicate their identity to curious spectators.

All winter the western rebels languished in jail. The next spring and summer they were tried for treason, speedily acquitted for the want of witnesses and lack of proof against them, and permitted to return to their homes.

In Philadelphia Alexander Hamilton sighed with satisfaction. "The new government has been tested and has proved itself victorious. Violent resistance to law has been curbed. The suppression of the insurrection has strengthened the federal government and increased our prestige at home and abroad. The government can now sustain itself. Federal authority has been vindicated!"

The whiskey rebellion was over.

.   .   .

John Harmon, disillusioned and emaciated from the long months in prison and the arduous journey over the mountains from Philadelphia, reached his home late in June. Amelia's face showed new lines and her mouth was set. The welcome in her eyes was shadowed with bitterness. When John asked her how things had gone through the winter and spring she told him of the insults of the soldiers who had been quartered down in their Mingo pasture, of their raids on the poultry house and the barn. The Harmons' meager winter supplies had dwindled long before the garden things had been ready; the weary struggle to prepare the muddy, tree-stump-studded fields for the spring planting had been climaxed by an accident to their last good horse.

John waited for her to mention the neighbors. Surely the Thomases had helped her. Finally:

"John, I just wouldn't let anybody help—why, the people around here are no better than traitors. All they care about is filling their purses ... "

"Amelia!"

"It's true. Morgan's soldiers stayed all winter. And because they had money—real gold and silver—to spend, everybody treated them with respect. They made friends with the militiamen. They weren't in prison . . . " and Amelia began to sob, all the loneliness and injustice welling up into her tears.

Next morning John went over to have a look at the fences around the north field. From his neighboring field Len Thomas hallooed. Shortly the two met.

"*Gazette* said you'd be home soon. Mighty glad to see you, John."

"How-do, Len."

"You look kind of peaked. I hear the food was pretty terrible. Good thing those Philadelphians couldn't see their way clear to keeping you and the rest any longer."

"Guess that's right, Len. How's the missis?"

"Oh, fine and dandy. Got my spring planting done early."

"What's this Amelia said about your selling the upper fields? Those were your best rye fields."

"Well, now," Len leaned comfortably against a post and pulled out his pipe. "I'll tell you, John. That fussing and fighting over the excise wasn't all to the bad. Thirteen thousand men are a powerful lot, and not all of them went back where they . . . "

"You mean those soldiers are still here! I thought . . . "

"No, no! You haven't got it right, John. A lot of them *stayed* here—settled down. Bought land and sent for their families!"

"So that's who you sold the field to!"

"Yes. One of the New Jersey militiamen. He's going to be a good neighbor, too. You'll like him, John."

"I don't know about that. What'd you do about your still?"

It developed that Len had done away with his still, as had most of the farmers. They were selling their grain to the large distillers, who could afford to concentrate on distilling and evading the tax collectors.

"That law won't ever be anything but a headache for Mr. Hamilton and our friends in Philadelphia," chuckled Len. "These big stillers now, they're always trading down river when the exciseman comes around. And a good Pittsburgh lawyer can tangle up a stiller's affairs so it looks like the exciseman owed him money, 'stead of him owing a tax!"

"I'm glad the whole thing's settled. There were times when it was mighty hard to tell right from wrong," John recalled. "Seems like when you get a crowd worked up nobody uses his good sense."

"Things seem to be clearing up pretty well. I'm not making so much on rye, but there's flax, now. We've a couple of new flax fields. There's a growing market for linen with so many new people in the district, and so many going through on their way west . . . "

"Len," broke in John. "Does everyone feel the way you do about the Insurrection and the excise?"

"No, not everybody. There's a good many selling their land and going down the river to Kentucky," replied Len slowly. "But the way I look at it, that law won't last forever, and this is real fine country around here. This section's going to be important because it's right at the head of the Ohio. People are starting West, and there's going to be a mighty good market in town for most everything we can raise, John."

"Not for me! Not for me, Len! You can have your profits and new neighbors. There's likely to be bad feeling around here for a good while. I think Amelia and I'll be moving on to where we can forget. Thank God, there's still Spanish land to the West, free land, and that's where we're going . . . "

About the Stories

PARENTS and teachers may welcome a word in explanation of some of the stories in this book. With the exception of the fourth, they are arranged in chronological order. "The Three Brothers" is the story of the earliest actual white settlement in western Pennsylvania of which there is any record. The Eckerlin brothers were outcasts from a religious colony at Ephrata, in Lancaster County, and they took up their abode some time between 1735 and 1754 on what has since become known as Dunkard Creek, in Greene County; extant records indicate that the settlement was destroyed by the French and Indians from Fort Duquesne.

George Croghan, the "King of the Traders," was perhaps the most famous, certainly the most active and important, of the white men who traded in the region during the middle eighteenth century. He played an important role during the French and Indian War, and later served as deputy Indian agent at Fort Pitt. His adventurous and romantic life has been fully told by Albert T. Volwiler in *George Croghan and the Westward Movement, 1741-1782*. The *Wilderness Trail*, by Charles A. Hanna, contains considerable material on Croghan and others who traded in this region and describes the routes they traversed.

The tale of unfinished Fort Prince George, which preceded the French fortress at the head of the Ohio River, is little known, but that of young Washington's heartbreaking battle at Fort Necessity has been heard often since the federal government reconstructed the temporary stockade and created Fort Necessity National Park, near Uniontown. Braddock's crushing defeat by the French and Indians is seen through the eyes of eighteen-year-old "James Smith, Captive" at Fort Duquesne. The captive's consequent life among the Indians is pictured in "Scoouwa the White Brother." Those who are interested in more details of his life will find one of the rare copies of Smith's journal in the Darlington Library at the University of

Pittsburgh, and Neil Swanson has retold the story in a recent novel, *The First Rebel.*

A lively controversy still exists as to whether or not Captain Jacobs was actually killed at the "Burning of Kittanning." Various points in the battle are indicated today by markers.

The names of General Forbes, Colonel Bouquet, and Major Grant are familiar to Pittsburghers as the names of streets. Some young people are probably also acquainted with the tablets on the court-house and at the blockhouse, and with the various Forbes Road markers along Fifth Avenue in Pittsburgh and along the Lincoln Highway east. A copy of Forbes's famous letter in which the name Pittsburgh is used for the first time may be seen at the Western Penn-sylvania Historical Society Building. A concise account of Forbes's march will be found in C. Hale Sipe's *Fort Ligonier and Its Times* and in Leland D. Baldwin's *Pittsburgh: The Story of a City.* Francis Parkman narrates the events of the French and Indian War with vivid detail in his *Montcalm and Wolfe:* chapter seven contains the story of Braddock's defeat and chapter twenty-two that of Forbes's expedition.

Part of Captain Trent's journal of the anxious days at Fort Pitt during 1763, when Pontiac's Indians laid siege, is printed in *Pen Pictures of Early Western Pennsylvania,* compiled by John W. Harp-ster. An exciting and detailed story of the whole Indian uprising is to be found in Parkman's *Pontiac's Conspiracy.* Swanson's *The Judas Tree* is a thrilling novel built around the attacks on Fort Pitt.

"When a Fist was Law" presents a picture of a typical frontier wed-ding and cabin raising and indicates the isolation of the small groups of settlers from any organized law enforcement. The story following, of how Dr. John Connolly seized Pittsburgh for Lord Dunmore, governor of Virginia, is an incident during the controversy that flared up in 1774 between Pennsylvania and Virginia over their western boundaries, and demonstrates even more vividly the difficulty of governing a frontier region. *Notes on the Settlements and Indian Wars,* by Dr. Joseph Doddridge, part of which is included in *Pen*

Pictures, is a readable and accurate contemporary account of pioneer life; and Agnes Sligh Turnbull's novel of the struggling descendants of Scotch-Irish pioneers in Westmoreland County, *The Rolling Years,* provides an absorbing sequel. Much of the humor and eccentricities in the daily lives of the settlers was chronicled in the pages of the community newspaper; and *Pittsburgh's Post Gazette,* by J. Cutler Andrews, contains excerpts from the early issues, as well as an entertaining account of the vicissitudes of printing and distributing a newspaper on the frontier.

Though little known, the long trek of the Eighth Pennsylvania Regiment east to join Washington in the winter of 1776-77 is one of the most heroic tales of the American Revolution. Aeneas Mackay, the leader, and many of his men succumbed in Quibbleton, New Jersey, as the result of exposure.

"Indians in the Valley" tells how in 1782 a band of Seneca under Guyasuta descended unexpectedly upon Hannastown, the county seat of Westmoreland, and sacked and burned the town. This was the last important Indian raid in the region, and twelve years later Wayne removed forever the danger of Indian attacks by defeating the red men at the battle of Fallen Timbers in Ohio. The description of the Hannastown raid given in the story is accurate, even to the names of the characters. This attack and numerous other depredations of the Indian war parties are described in *Indian Chiefs* and *Indian Wars* of Pennsylvania by C. Hale Sipe. *Moccasins in the Wilderness,* Elizabeth Hawthorne Buck's novel for children, describes aspects of relations between the Indians and the white men and presents a faithful picture of early days on the frontier.

"Elder Smiley Volunteers" is an almost unbelievable incident out of the records of the Redstone Presbytery. "Liberty and Learning" is, of course, the story of the humble beginnings of the University of Pittsburgh and of Hugh Henry Brackenridge, one of Pittsburgh's most famous sons. Henry M. Brackenridge's *Recollections of Persons and Places in the West* and Agnes L. Starrett's *Through One Hundred and Fifty Years: The University of Pittsburgh* tell more of the story.

The main events of the Whiskey Insurrection of 1794, the first major internal crisis that the new federal government of the United States had to face, are related in the final tale. The incidents happened over a period of years, but here they are compressed and personalized. The whole affair excited much comment and a number of accounts were written by the leading actors. To the present day, in those counties where most of the action took place, arguments wax pro and con. The best short account of the affair is in *The Whiskey Rebellion,* by Richard T. Wiley, who has also fictionized the story in *Sim Greene and Tom the Tinker's Men.* Another novel is that by Henry C. Cook, *The Latimers, A Tale of the Western Insurrection of 1794.*

The pages of the *Western Pennsylvania Historical Magazine* and of the *Pennsylvania Magazine of History and Biography* are replete with incidents such as those narrated in this book. A handy reference book and one that will give credence to the stories by identifying and locating places mentioned in them is the *Guidebook to Historic Places in Western Pennsylvania* prepared by the Western Pennsylvania Historical Survey. Clarence E. Macartney's two volumes, *Not Far From Pittsburgh* and *Right Here in Pittsburgh* will also be of interest to readers of this book.